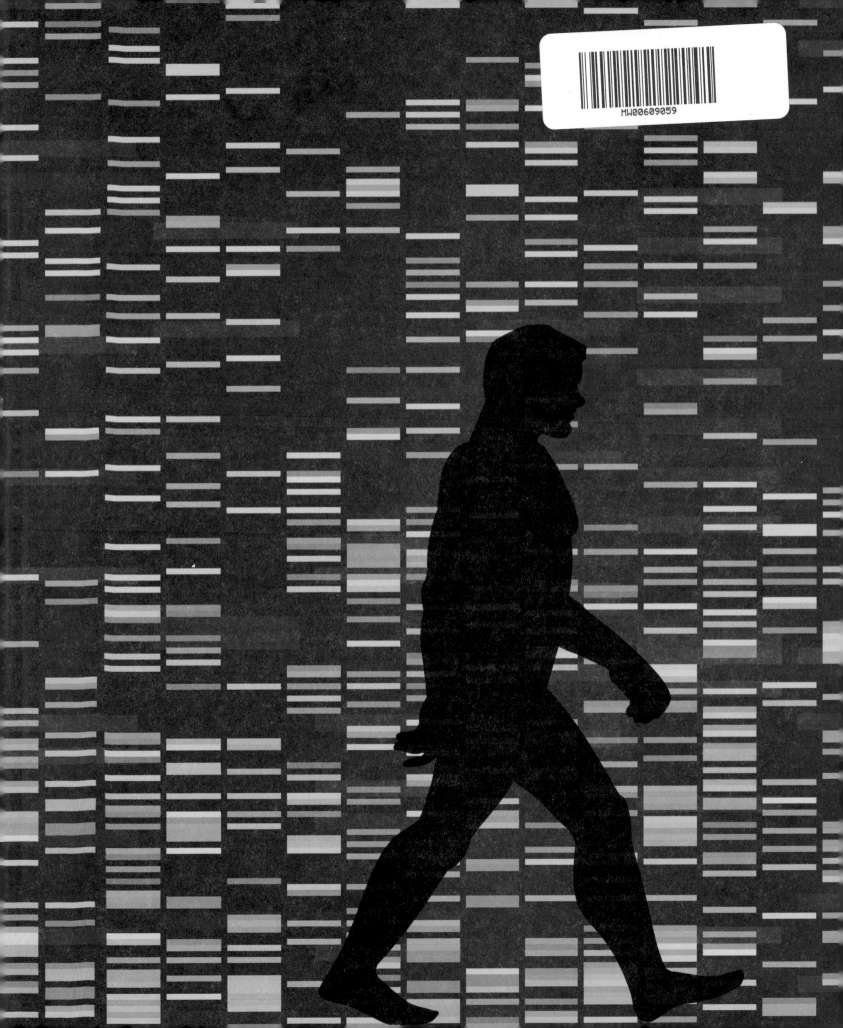

MW00609059

CHIMPS AND
HUMANS

*A Geneticist Discovers DNA Evidence
That Challenges Evolution*

CHIMPS AND HUMANS

A Geneticist Discovers DNA Evidence
That Challenges Evolution

Jeffrey P. Tomkins

INSTITUTE FOR CREATION RESEARCH

Dallas, Texas
ICR.org

CHIMPS AND HUMANS

A Geneticist Discovers DNA Evidence That Challenges Evolution

by Dr. Jeffrey P. Tomkins

First printing: August 2021

Copyright © 2021 by the Institute for Creation Research. All rights reserved. No portion of this book may be used in any form without written permission of the publisher, with the exception of brief excerpts in articles and reviews. For more information, write to Institute for Creation Research, P. O. Box 59029, Dallas, TX 75229.

Series concept and direction: Jayme Durant, ICR Director of Communications
Senior Editor: Beth Mull
Editors: Lori Fausak, Michael Stamp, Christy Hardy, Truett Billups
Graphic Designer: Susan Windsor
Cover image: BigstockPhoto.com

All Scripture quotations are from the New King James Version.

ISBN: 978-1-946246-35-6
Library of Congress Control Number: 2021939759

Please visit our website for other books and resources: ICR.org

Printed in the United States of America.

TABLE OF CONTENTS

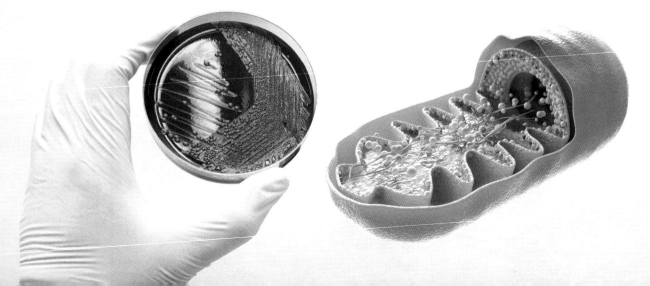

FOREWORD

Chimps and Humans: A Geneticist Discovers DNA Evidence That Challenges Evolution was written by Dr. Jeff Tomkins, who is my friend and colleague. We are both experts in in our respective fields of genetics, have both spent most of our careers as full-time research scientists, and later in our careers have both spent many years critically examining ape-to-man evolutionary claims. Unlike myself, Dr. Tomkins is an expert in DNA sequencing and is a very well-credentialed genomicist. He is uniquely qualified to write this book.

For over 150 years, evolutionists have insisted that humans evolved from apes. During the last few decades it has been claimed that ape-to-man evolution can best be proven by using genetic arguments. However, there has been a great deal of monkey business associated with these genetic claims.

Initially, the primary genetic argument for ape-to-man was very simple—apes and men were said to be almost identical genetically. Over time, evolutionists have developed numerous layers of argumentation in order to fortify and expand their assertion that ape and man are almost identical genetically. These arguments have seemed compelling to many so that countless Christians have compromised their faith or have walked away from their faith.

Dr. Tomkins has carefully investigated all of the various arguments supporting ape-to-man evolution. On every level, he has discovered that the supposedly compelling evolutionary arguments for ape-to-man evolution do not withstand careful scrutiny. More than this, he shows that there has been monkey business associated with the aggressive marketing of human evolution by the media and many high-profile scientists. The evolutionists, because of their ideological commitment to human evolution, have consistently manipulated or misrepresented their data to force-fit it into the ideologically correct narrative. Dr. Tomkins documents this on many levels.

Dr. Tomkins shows that DNA similarity was a false narrative from the beginning. It began late in the last century with the use of extremely crude measurements of how different DNAs melt and stick together. This method was simply not valid, but it was used to suggest that man and chimp were 98 to 99% similar, creating the desired narrative. This methodology was quickly discarded within the evolutionary community. However, they still held on to the claim of 98 to 99% similarity, which was conveniently and widely enshrined as the ultimate proof of ape-to-man evolution.

With the emergence of valid DNA sequencing, the most similar parts of the ape and human genomes were chosen for comparison. Dr. Tomkins shows these early comparisons very greatly exaggerated the DNA similarity. There was clearly very strong bias in the early data, which favored the enshrined 98 to 99% similarity. This systematic bias continues even today.

I believe that Dr. Tomkins has masterfully set the record straight. It turns out that comparing genomes is very complex and often requires geneticists to compare apples to oranges. To try and work around this problem, most genomicists have used programs that force alignment of two different DNA sequences, even when some parts do not actually align at all. They do this to "unscramble the puzzle," which makes the two genomes seem much more similar than they really are. Dr. Tomkins uses a better strategy that involves random sampling of sequences in one genome and then finding the true alignment in the other genome. In many cases, he finds that for a given sequence in one genome there simply is no counterpart in the other genome.

Dr. Tomkins' analyses consistently show that chimp-human similarity is in the range of 80 to 90%. This means that the genetic differences are at least tenfold greater than advertised. This represents at least 300 million nucleotide differences that separate chimp from man. Remarkably, honest secular scientists are now reporting the very same findings! I am convinced that Dr. Tomkins has done the best genetic analysis of the chimp-human similarities and differences. Arguably, he has delved into this complex issue in much more depth than most evolutionists.

Dr. Tomkins has gone way beyond the issue of just percent similarity. He has delved deeply into the other levels of chimp-human genetic differences. In every case, whenever Dr. Tomkins has dug deep he has been able to overthrow the claims of the evolutionists.

In particular, Dr. Tomkins has completely overthrown the famous claims of Dr. Kenneth Miller regarding the reputed chromosome 2 "fusion" (chapter 4). He shows that while the chimp and human Y chromosomes should be almost nearly identical, they are actually so different that they alone are sufficient to falsify chimp-to-human evolution (chapter 5). He shows that a significant fraction of human genes are "orphan genes" that are unique to man and are not found in chimp or any other primate (chapter 6).

Likewise, he has totally overthrown the claims that pseudogenes are "dead fossil genes" that prove shared mistakes (chapter 7). He shows that while parts of the human genome are unique to man, other parts of the human genome most closely line up with either orangutan, gorilla, or chimpanzee. This produces an evolutionary tree that is backwards, with chimps most distant from man and orangutan closest (chapter 8). He shows that even those chimp and human genes that are very similar are actually consistently very different in their *biological function* and their *genetic regulation* (chapter 9).

Even more remarkable, he shows that above and beyond the elaborate genetic systems of both man and ape, there are numerous epigenetic systems that constitute multiple information systems on higher levels. He shows that these higher epigenetic systems are profoundly different in man versus ape (chapter 10). He shows that genetic "clocks" do not work when calibrated using evolutionary assumptions, but when calibrated using known mutation rates, genetic clocks clearly show that man, apes, and other creatures arose recently, so there simply has not been enough time for ape-to-man evolution (chapter 11). He also shows how the out-of-Africa story fails (chapter 12). Most amazing of all, all of these genetic problems that are associated with the ape-to-man evolution story go away if we simply accept the biblical narrative (chapter 13).

Dr. Tomkins' work is very, very impressive, and remarkably both qualified Christian scientists and honest secular scientists are now getting very similar results. I urge open-minded scientists to examine Dr. Tomkins' findings.

John C. Sanford
Retired Cornell University geneticist
Author, *Genetic Entropy & the Mystery of the Genome*

ACKNOWLEDGMENTS

I would like to first thank our mighty triune Creator God, who made all things through Christ Jesus my Lord, for giving me the opportunity to have an impact for His kingdom in debunking the lies of this present age and glorifying our mighty God who created humankind in His image.

Secondly, I would like to honor and thank the late Dr. Henry Morris III, former CEO of the Institute for Creation Research, for hiring me in 2009 to work at ICR, and who also specifically commissioned me at the beginning of my tenure to study the alleged human-chimp DNA similarity issue that at that point had not been adequately addressed in the creation science movement.

I would also like to thank my creationist colleagues Dr. Jerry Bergman and Dr. Nathaniel Jeanson, who not only have worked with me over the years on this important topic but have also been staunch supporters of my work in various critical ways. I would also like to heartily thank current ICR President Dr. Randy Guliuzza, who has also supported and encouraged me over the years and who is now enabling my work to go beyond debunking the false notion of high human-chimp DNA similarity to begin highlighting the amazing adaptive engineering of the human body that gives glory to the Creator who rightly deserves all the credit.

And finally, I would like to thank my lovely and godly wife, Ann Tomkins, whose prayers and encouragement make my effective ministry for the Lord and His kingdom possible.

Introduction

In 2005, the first draft of the chimpanzee genome was published with the bold assertion "We calculate the genome-wide nucleotide divergence between human and chimpanzee to be 1.23%."[1] In other words, it was claimed that human and chimp DNA were 98.8% similar. Yet only three years earlier in 2002, a research lab reported that it had sequenced about 9,000 random pieces of chimp DNA for a total of 1.9 million bases and stated that only "about two thirds could be unambiguously aligned to DNA sequences in humans" and "for 7% of the chimpanzee sequences, no region with similarity could be detected in the human genome."[2] So, how did they get from only about two thirds of chimp DNA sequence able to be accurately matched onto human and a significant 7% having absolutely no match to it being nearly identical? Clearly there was some monkey business going on.

Then after years of the general public being told we were less than 2% different in our DNA compared to a chimp, one of the leading primate evolutionists in the world came out of the closet in 2012 and stated, "It is now clear that the genetic differences between humans and chimpanzees are far more extensive than previously thought; their genomes are not 98% or 99% identical."[3] He then went on to say that the highly similar regions were about 96% identical, not including the other regions that were much less similar. More recently in 2018, the newest version of the chimpanzee genome was compared to human with the result that "the percentage of nucleotides in the human genome that had one-to-one exact matches in the chimpanzee genome was 84.38%."[4] So now even by the admissions of evolutionists we have gone from 98.8% similarity to about 84%.

Since the first original claims of high human-chimp DNA similarity were made by evolutionists going back to early experiments in the 1970s, many exciting scientific developments in the debate have occurred, and none of them have been favorable to the evolutionary paradigm that is the topic of this book. But first it's important to share a bit of my story, particularly from the perspective of a scientist objectively seeking answers and not really knowing what I would discover along the way.

My Human-Chimp Paradigm Journey

I obtained my Ph.D. in genetics from Clemson University in 1996, performing my doctoral research in quantitative and physiological genetics. Following my Ph.D., I got a job working as a post-doc in a public genomics institute at Clemson. I eventually ended up as the director of the institute and a faculty member in the Department of Genetics and Biochemistry.

In addition to teaching undergraduate and graduate-level classes in genetics and genomics, my academic career involved many exciting and well-funded research projects studying all sorts of strange creatures, including platypuses, fire ants, ticks, shrimp, oysters, flies, and a variety of different plants. I was blessed to have published 57 refereed secular journal papers in genetics, genomics, cell biology, and proteomics, along with seven secular book chapters in genomics and molecular biology during this period of my life.

Many people are surprised to know that despite this rather thorough background in the field of genetics and genomics, I never once questioned or pondered the human-chimp DNA similarity paradigm. I was basically too busy studying the DNA of everything else. Although I realized that Darwinian macroevolution was a highly speculative paradigm with very little hard evidence to back it up, human and ape DNA were just not on my radar during my secular academic career.

So what happened to my perspective on the human-chimp paradigm and why this book? After spending over 20 years studying and working within the highly controlled academic confines of political correctness based on the religion of evolution, I felt that I needed to direct what remained of my life and talents exploring the truth in science at the Institute for Creation Research. Because many people in churches want answers to the evolutionary propaganda of human evolution, I was immediately confronted with the issue of human origins. Chief among the icons of human evolution is the supposed human-ape evolutionary dogma constantly nagging at the faith of Christians and their biblical belief in a Creator who made mankind in His image as the pinnacle act of the creation week recorded in Genesis.

At the time, I was already aware that very little support existed in the DNA sequence data for Darwinian macroevolution because the diverse types of plants and animals I had studied showed distinct genetic discontinuity, which fit well with the biblical paradigm that every living creature was created "after their kind" (Genesis 1). However, the alleged nearly identical DNA similarity between chimpanzee and human as popularized by the media, scientists, and even some professing Christian scientific authorities was clearly a key issue that needed additional scrutiny and research. At first the task seemed intimidating, but the deeper I investigated the published scientific literature and even performed my own genetic analyses, the more it became clear that much of the human-chimp DNA similarity data had been filtered, manipulated, cherry-picked, and even obfuscated to measure up to an academic gold standard amounting to nothing more than political correctness in accordance with the religion of evolution.

Since the era when Charles Darwin published his various evolutionary works in the late 1800s, including his racist book on human evolution *The Descent of Man, and Selection in Relation to Sex*, the concept that humans evolved from apes has remained a central theme in the origins debate. While the quest to find the "missing link" between humans and apes in the fossil record continues to move forward in confusion, desperation, and obfuscation, theoretical evolutionists are supposedly providing us with evidence that we are not more than just a few DNA sequences away from being a chimp. Or at least that's what the popular media, some secular scientists, and the enigmatic Christian evolutionists are telling us.

A common claim among such evolutionists is that the DNA of humans and chimps is about 98 to 99% similar. The truth of the whole matter is that the DNA evidence supporting similarity between humans and chimps is manipulated to fit an evolutionary mold just as the supposed fossil evidence for hominid evolution has been over the years. However, unlike the fragmented and highly subjective nature of hominid fossils, DNA data are increasing in accuracy, quantity, and completeness, which is resulting in a day of reckoning and demise for evolution, including human evolution.

So what would actually be the end result in the quest of a well-trained genomics and bioinformatics scientist like myself who aggressively analyzed the various research publications and raw DNA sequence data without being restricted by the chains of academic political correctness tied to an evolutionary naturalist presupposition in regard to human origins? This book is an up-to-date synopsis of such an effort that has now entailed over nine years of research and analysis.

Important note: Obviously, if you are reading this book, you have some interest and enthusiasm for research in DNA science and perhaps also an interest in the subject of human origins. For those readers of this book who need a quick introduction to DNA science and the expanding field of genomics, please go to the DNA primer in appendix A of this book to get yourself up to speed on the subject.

References

1. The Chimpanzee Sequencing and Analysis Consortium. 2005. Initial sequence of the chimpanzee genome and comparison with the human genome. *Nature*. 437 (7055): 69-87.

2. Ebersberger, I. et al. 2002. Genomewide Comparison of DNA Sequences between Humans and Chimpanzees. *American Journal of Human Genetics*. 70 (6): 1490-1497.

3. Preuss, T. M. 2012. Human brain evolution: From gene discovery to phenotype discovery. *Proceedings of the National Academy of Sciences*. 109: 10709-10716.

4. Buggs, R. How similar are human and chimpanzee genomes? Posted on richardbuggs.com July 14, 2018, accessed August 9, 2018.

1 Human-Chimp DNA Similarity Origins

Summary: The idea that humans are connected to apes had its roots in the ancient pagan idea of a chain of being that was a precursor to Darwin's more advanced synthesis of humans evolving from apes. In the early days of modern molecular biology nearly a century after Darwin, a crude form of DNA comparison called reassociation kinetics seemed to support the contention that humans are very similar to chimpanzees. This close level of similarity, originally estimated at about 98.5%, became a gold standard to which all subsequent human-chimpanzee DNA research paid homage.

A widely popularized claim used to bolster the myth of human evolution from an ape-like ancestor is that the DNA of chimpanzees (chimps) and humans is nearly identical. Some scientists and academics have even suggested that humans and chimps are nothing more than two different species that should actually be placed in the same genus. It's even claimed by some that chimps should have the same rights and status as humans. This chapter develops the history and origins of the ideology of how chimps achieved the status of becoming our so-called closest living ancestor and the early and crude DNA-based discoveries that kicked off the nearly identical DNA dogma.

Darwinian Ideas about Man's Origins

So, how did chimps get placed within the evolutionary dogma of humans evolving from apes to begin with? One of the initial contributions to the human-chimp evolutionary paradigm was unwittingly grounded in the work of English anatomist Edward Tyson and his colleague William Cowper. Ashley Montagu, the notable British-American anthropologist, evolutionist, and anti-creationist, describes the event for us.

> In the spring of 1698, the English anatomist Edward Tyson obtained the remains of a young chimpanzee. The animal had been brought to England aboard a ship bound from Angola, but it contracted an infection en route and died soon after its arrival. Together with his friend and colleague William Cowper, an expert on muscle anatomy, Tyson dissected this chimpanzee and published his findings in the 1699 book *Orang-Outang, Sive Homo sylvestris*, or, *The Anatomy of a Pigmie*. Tyson's work was the first scientific description of the complete anatomy of a chimpanzee.[1]

Tyson noticed a general anatomical resemblance between the chimp and humans, and he interpreted this similarity in terms of the chain of being, a popular philosophy of the day employed by Tyson based on an ancient pagan paradigm that formed the groundwork for the evolutionary ideas of Charles Darwin. In this chain of being concept, which is nearly identical to Aristotle's *Scala Naturae*, living creatures form a progressively complex linear continuum with mankind at the very top. Darwin historian, American anthropologist, educator, philosopher, and natural science writer Loren Eiseley, in his book *Darwin's Century*, states the following.[2]

> All that the Chain of Being actually needed to become a full-fledged evolutionary theory was the introduction into it of the conception

of time in vast quantities added to mutability of form. It demanded, in other words, a universe not made but being made continuously.[2]

In regard to Tyson's chimpanzee specimen, he interpreted his anatomical observations within the paradigm of the chain of being, the philosophical foundation of the Darwinian synthesis. Tyson describes his thought processes as quoted by Montagu.

> Thus in the Ape and Monkey-kind, Aristotle's Cebus [monkey] I look upon to be a degree above his Cynocephalus [lemur]; and his Pithecus or Ape above his Cebus, and our Pygmie [chimpanzee] a higher degree above any of them, we yet know, and more resembling a Man: But at the same time I take him to be wholly a Brute, tho' in the formation of the Body, and in the Sensitive or Brutal Soul, it may be, more resembling a Man, than any other Animal; so that in this Chain of the Creation, as an intermediate Link between an Ape and a Man, I would place our Pygmie.[1]

Some have proposed that Tyson stated this within the context of some sort of biblical creation paradigm. However, this idea is most likely not the case. Tyson cites the naturalistic pagan writings of Aristotle and indicates that the chimp was "an intermediate link" as part of the "chain of creation."[1] The chain of being idea is a hierarchal concept of the spectrum of life within an ancient pagan paradigm and is without much doubt the philosophical precursor to the system of evolution promoted by Darwin.

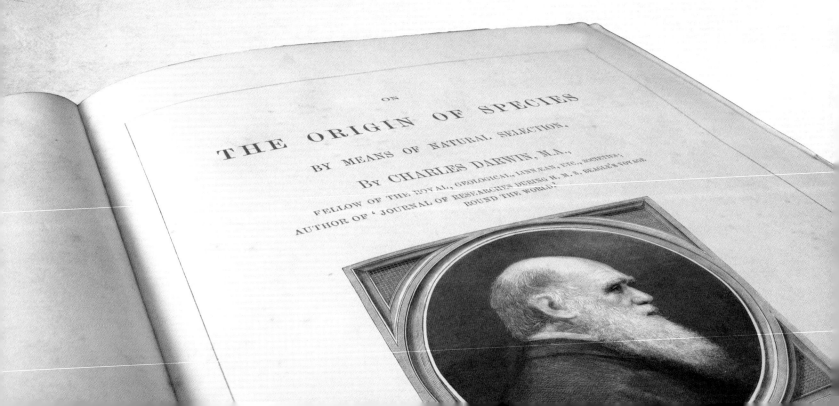

In addition, many philosophers and mystics, both modern and ancient, believe that mankind is evolving (also referred to as "becoming") into a form of godhood or an enlightened perfected state of being. It is believed that this becoming happens progressively as people acquire more and more hidden knowledge analogous to mysterious evolutionary transitions. In fact, Darwin repeatedly used the word becoming as a synonym for evolutionary progress throughout his evolutionary writings.[3] The term becoming would have been very familiar to Darwin in his day as the Anglo elite circles in which he was immersed commonly used the notion of it in their speeches and writings.[4]

While not the chief aim of this chapter, it should be noted that this precursor to and the current sister philosophy of modern Darwinian evolution has been around since ancient times and remains popular to this day.[4] In fact, the primary philosophy supporting the trans-humanist movement of today is undergirded by the premise that humans must take charge of their own evolution and advance to the next evolutionary level of becoming gods using advanced technology.

The most important point of all this is that the idea of man evolving or becoming was not suddenly invented by Darwin but ultimately involves deep philosophical roots in secular thought that can be traced even further back in time before the Greek philosophers to ancient Babylon, as described quite thoroughly by the late Dr. Henry Morris in his excellent work *The Long War Against God*.[5]

Early Evidence for DNA Similarity?

The first estimates of high human-chimp DNA similarity were derived from a field of biochemical research popular in the 1970s and early 1980s termed "reassociation kinetics." Initial reports using this type of technology were the basis for claims by popular evolutionary proponents like Richard Dawkins, who stated in 1986 that chimps and humans "share more than 99 percent of our genes."[6] When Dawkin's statement was published, his comment was not based on actual DNA sequence data but on the indirect methodology of reassociation kinetics. At the time, accurate estimates for gene numbers in humans and chimps were not known because high-throughput DNA sequencing, the trademark technology of the genomics era, had not even become a reality.

The automation of DNA sequencing and other related technologies that allowed

DNA sequencing lab circa 2010–2012

the genomics revolution to get going began to appear in the 1990s. The first draft of the human genome was published in 2001, followed by a more complete version in 2004, and then the rough draft of the chimp genome in 2005.[7-9]

The supposed high DNA similarity being touted in the 1980s was based on an indirect estimate using a methodology called reassociation kinetics. This technique relies on heat or chemistry to separate (denature) the double-stranded DNA into separate single-stranded molecules like unzipping a zipper. When the DNA is allowed to reassociate (recombine) and zip back up in a slow and controlled process by complimentary base-pairing, various fractions of the genome based on their DNA sequence complexity can be recovered. The general principle of how this works operates as follows: the slower the reassociation, the more complex the sequence and the more gene-dense the DNA is. In general, three classes of DNA can be extracted by this process: 1) high-copy DNA is mostly composed of highly repetitive sequences and has a low number of genes, 2) low-copy DNA which is moderately repetitive with moderate levels of genes, and 3) single-copy DNA that is gene dense.

For studies where two different types of creatures are compared, the single-copy gene-dense fraction is extracted such as from human and chimp. These gene-dense fractions from both human and chimp are then mixed together. The DNA mixture is then disassociated and allowed to reassociate in a controlled manner. The level and rate of reassociation based on complementary base-matching between the two human and chimp gene-dense fractions are then indirectly measured. These rates are compared to control experiments, which is the rate of reassociation for the DNA of a single organism (non-mixed).

The caveat of this type of experiment is that only the single-copy portions of the genomes are used to calculate the estimates of similarity. This fraction represents less than 5% of the total DNA in the genome. Scientists target the single-copy portion based on the high gene content it contains. At the time, it was believed that the rest of the genome was randomly evolving and unimportant, hence the phrase "junk DNA" was used to describe much of it.

There are important things to consider with these types of experiments that help explain their results in light of recent genomic discoveries. First, we now realize that many genes are located in the other two genome fractions and were therefore omitted from these early experiments. Another important point is that the past decade of research has shown that virtually the entire genome is now known to be functional. Even areas of the genome that are in-between genes contain many important control features and genes that code for long RNAs.[10,11]

The long-standing hypothesis that the parts of the genome that do not code for proteins are the regions that are largely responsible for many of the creature-specific aspects of DNA is now being widely confirmed in the sequencing of many animals and plants. The emerging genetic model is that many of the standard protein-coding genes present in genomes that perform basic biochemical functions are often not as creature specific but operate more like essential genetic building blocks. Hence, it is these types of common code regions that are very similar between types of creatures that are highly represented in the single-copy class of DNA.

The original 99% nearly identical DNA similarity boast, which secular evolutionary writer Cohen later called "The Myth of 1%," was prompted in 1975 by Allen Wilson and Mary-Claire King using the reassociation kinetics methodology discussed above.[12,13] Other studies using reassociation kinetics methodology produced similar outcomes but at a slightly higher level of difference of about 1.5%, thus producing the widely claimed statements of 98.5% DNA sequence similarity between humans and chimps.[14,15]

Even though reassociation studies omitted over 95% of the total DNA in an experiment, evolutionists were still surprised at the high levels of similarity being observed in the single-copy gene-rich component of the genome. This astonishment was due to the fact that very obvious large physical differences existed between humans and chimps that did not correlate with their initial estimates of high DNA similarity. This conundrum resulted in the eventual widely held belief, as noted by evolutionary writer Gibbons, that the huge differences between humans and chimps in anatomy and behavior were best explained by very small genetic differences.[16]

A Dogmatic Gold Standard Is Set

A historical analysis of these early published reports for human and chimp DNA comparison based on reassociation kinetics technology shows that a 98.5% DNA similarity gold standard had been set for the human evolution research community. As a result of this officially set benchmark, DNA sequence similarity research in the subsequent genomics era that was soon to follow conformed accordingly through a process of data filtering and manipulation. Nearly all of the genetics and genomics papers in

“As a member of the secular academic community for many years at a large public research university, I am very familiar with the fact that group conformity to such academic mantras and paradigms is necessary to obtain success in grantsmanship, publishing, academic tenure, and overall job security.”

the 21st century studying the DNA similarity issue between humans and chimps have given unwavering authoritative homage to these initial DNA reassociation kinetics reports in their introductory material.

As will be shown throughout much of this book, these more recent DNA similarity research reports using the tools of modern genetics show pervasive evidence of data filtering and exclusion in their analyses to obtain results that would adhere to the 98 to 99% DNA similarity gold standard. As a member of the secular academic community for many years at a large public research university, I am very familiar with the fact that group conformity to such academic mantras and paradigms is necessary to obtain success in grantsmanship, publishing, academic tenure, and overall job security.

As will be demonstrated in the following chapter, the omitted and obfuscated data related to these more recent genomics reports reveal that the DNA of humans and chimps is not nearly as similar as often touted by those promoting the evolutionary agenda.

References

1. Montagu, M. F. A. 1943. Edward Tyson, M. D., F. R. S. 1650-1708 and the rise of human and comparative anatomy in England. *Memoirs of the American Philosophical Society.* XX: 1-487.
2. Eiseley, L. 1958. *Darwin's Century.* Garden City, NY: Doubleday.
3. Darwin, C. 1871. *The Descent of Man, and Selection in Relation to Sex.* London: John Murray.
4. Collins, P. D. and P. D. Collins. 2006. *The Ascendancy of the Scientific Dictatorship: An Examination of Epistemic Autocracy, From the 19th to the 20th Century.* Charleston, SC: BookSurge Publishing.
5. Morris, H. 2000. *The Long War Against God: The History and Impact of the Creation/Evolution Conflict.* Green Forest, AR: Master Books.
6. Dawkins, R. 1986. *The Blind Watchmaker: Why the Evidence of Evolution Reveals a Universe Without Design.* New York: W. W. Norton.
7. International Human Genome Sequencing Consortium. 2001. Initial sequencing and analysis of the human genome. *Nature.* 409: 861-920.
8. Venter, J. C. et al. 2001. The sequence of the human genome. *Science.* 291: 1304-1351.
9. The Chimpanzee Sequencing and Analysis Consortium. 2005. Initial sequence of the chimpanzee genome and comparison with the human genome. *Nature.* 437: 69-87.
10. Wells, J. 2011. *The Myth of Junk DNA.* Seattle, WA: Discovery Institute Press.
11. The ENCODE Project Consortium. 2012. An Integrated Encyclopedia of DNA Elements in the Human Genome. *Nature.* 489 (7414): 57-74.
12. Cohen, J. 2007. Relative differences: the myth of 1%. *Science.* 316: 1836.
13. King, M. C. and A. C. Wilson. 1975. Evolution at two levels in humans and chimpanzees. *Science.* 188: 107–116.
14. Hoyer B. H. et al. 1972. Examination of hominid evolution by DNA sequence homology. *Journal Human Evolution.* 1: 645-649.
15. Sibley, C. G. and J. E. Ahlquist. 1984. The phylogeny of the hominoid primates, as indicated by DNA-DNA hybridization. *Journal of Molecular Evolution.* 20: 2-15.
16. Gibbons, A. 1998. Which of our genes make us human? *Science.* 281: 1432-1434.

2 Modern Genomics and Human-Chimp DNA Similarity

Summary: As DNA sequencing became more advanced, evolutionary studies were undertaken to compare human to chimpanzee by analyzing actual DNA sequence. However, scientists realized that to uphold the 98.5% DNA similarity gold standard, they needed to cherry-pick the highly similar data and throw out data that did not fit the dogma. In evolutionary research publications where the discarded data could be factored back into the analysis, human-chimpanzee DNA similarities were only 66 to 86%, depending on the study.

As research in the modern genomics era began to unfold, it began to appear that new discoveries in chimpanzee DNA sequence might actually support the earlier claims of high similarity discovered by studies done using reassociation kinetics mentioned in the previous chapter. Or at least, that is what was often reported.

At the initial stages of my quest to get to the bottom of the thorny issue of human-chimp DNA similarity, as any good scientist would, I did a thorough literature review of the topic at hand. I began by re-evaluating the scientific literature that supposedly undergirded these claims. One of the first things I noticed is that almost every research paper paid unwavering homage to the seemingly high 98.5% DNA similarity between humans and chimps supposedly established by the indirect and rather crude method of reassociation kinetics research described in chapter 1, which apparently had become the gold standard for any further endeavors. And as I got into the nitty gritty details of the materials and methods of these papers, it quickly became apparent that results being obtained in the new "genomics era" were manipulated to conform to the gold standard using a variety of techniques and tricks that included the discarding of nonsimilar data and a focus on only those DNA segments that were highly similar. The end result was a false picture of chimp DNA appearing more human-like than it really was.[1,2]

Omitting Nonsimilar Data

One of the first human-chimp DNA sequence comparison papers was actually published by one of the original pioneers in DNA reassociation kinetics, Roy Britten.[3] The research study compared the sequence of five different large chunks of chimp DNA known to have corresponding regions in the human genome. The chimp DNA segments selected in this study were some of the first regions of the chimp genome selected for sequencing because of their known similarity to human DNA. This is a commonly utilized cherry-picking technique used to enhance DNA similarity estimates. Researchers will often only analyze highly similar preselected DNA segments between

two organisms, which not only makes the sequence similarity easier to determine but does not really represent a fair sampling across the whole genome. In all fairness to Dr. Britten, my personal communications with him revealed that the sequences he used were about the only ones available at the time in 2002, so I am not blaming him for their previous biased selection for sequencing. Nevertheless, the DNA was selected and sequenced by a separate research group based on their known predetermined high similarity to human.

The total length of the five different chimp DNA segments analyzed by Britten was 846,016 bases. However, only 92% was similar enough to human to allow the algorithm to make the comparison. In other words, 8% of the DNA was excluded from the analysis because it would not match at all. For the DNA that did match, a DNA sequence similarity of 95% was reported. However, a more accurate estimate would include the complete sequence of all five chimp DNA segments, including what was excluded, giving a more realistic overall DNA similarity of only 87%. For a depiction of how two DNA sequences are compared for similarity, see Figure 1 below.

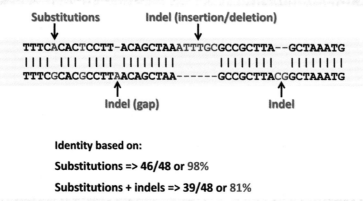

Figure 1. A hypothetical match (alignment) between similar DNA sequences from two different creatures (Seq1 and Seq2). In nearly all alignments there are portions of compared sequences outside the alignment region that are typically omitted but can also represent valid differences. Substitutions are single-base changes where the DNA letter is different. Insertions and deletions called indels are small gaps between the two sequences. Indels can vary in size from a single base to thousands of bases. Indels larger than a few bases in size are typically not accounted for in alignments.

Another notable study used chimp DNA sequence obtained from supposedly random DNA fragments that were about 300 to 600 bases in length.[4] These small chimp DNA fragments were compared to one of the earlier versions of the human genome. It is noteworthy that only about 67% of the chimp DNA fragments could be accurately

matched onto human, and the length of the matches is not given. And as near as I can tell from the materials and methods section of the paper, the researchers used an algorithm that did not include small gaps in the DNA sequence. Thus, the researchers only included the smallest of differences in single bases between human and chimp for very small chunks of similar areas that were highly identical. So basically the algorithm stops when it hits a gap, with the end result being that the nonsimilar gaps are not included. As a result of this highly selective methodology, the final cherry-picked data produced estimates of 98.5% DNA sequence similarity. In reality, huge amounts of nonsimilar data had been discarded to achieve these biased results.

Unfortunately, the disturbing technique of discarding nonsimilar data and cherry-picking highly similar data when comparing human and chimp DNA became a common and accepted practice among researchers. These highly biased research practices have produced the scientific fodder that the popular media has fed upon to bolster the human evolution story.

Another problem with the whole human-chimp DNA similarity paradigm is obfuscation. If the cherry-picking of highly similar data combined with discarding nonsimilar DNA in human-chimp comparisons was not bad enough, key data along with the methods needed to verify the results and calculate more accurate and objective overall similarities by outside researchers are consistently omitted. I personally have found that in a study of the top human-chimpanzee DNA similarity studies published between 2002 and 2005, three out the seven papers contained no information on the amount of data that did not match or specific information on how the analysis was conducted so the study could be repeated.[1]

Data Cherry-Picking Tricks

Another disturbing trend I immediately noticed upon studying the literature is that only selective parts of common genes were used. Just like a computer programmer will use common words and phrases between computer programs that do completely different things, we find the same principle in the genetic code among living things. Because humans, apes, and even other mammals have generally similar basic biochemistries for many fundamental life processes, the genes that encode the proteins needed for these systems would be expected to be highly similar. Evolutionists were consistently using the most common mammalian genetic code from protein-coding genes to make comparisons between humans and chimps.

The concept of what constitutes a gene is now highly complicated due to the unfolding complexity of the genome. We now know that a gene can either code for a protein or a functional RNA molecule. In fact, there are over five times as many RNA-coding genes in the genome as there are protein-coding genes. In the old school view, genes simply coded for proteins. Within protein-coding genes, only a small portion of that sequence actually codes for protein. Scientists now estimate that less than 3% of the human genome codes for protein.

The coding parts of protein-coding genes are called exons and also happen to be the most similar parts of the genome and the most favorable to promote an evolutionary worldview. Thus, it is no surprise that evolutionists have focused on these regions of the genome in their comparative studies between human and chimp. Typical of the trend to only align exon sequences, one notable study compared only human and chimp protein-coding regions using only 97 exon fragments.[7] To show the level of the bias in this sample, there are actually more than 234,000 protein-coding exons in the human genome,[8] so this is hardly a valid genome-wide sample. Adding even more bias is the fact that the exons were prescreened based on the criterion that they were known to be highly similar in both humans and chimps. Because of the shocking lack of detail in the reported methodology in the paper, it's impossible to obtain a clear estimate of actual DNA similarity achieved in this particular study.

Another high-profile study of a very similar nature used nearly identical methodology, and once again no data were given to allow the calculation of overall similarity to repeat the results.[9] Of the total starting number of exon sequences in this particular research project (20,361), the researchers did disclose that they discarded 33% in an ambiguously stated yet revealing "very conservative quality control."[9] In other words, the chimp sequences that got tossed out were not similar enough and either would not align to human or did so very poorly.

The one noteworthy and common feature of these highly biased studies is the fact that researchers routinely discard about one third of the chimpanzee sequence in their analyses because it is too nonsimilar and will not match up well with human DNA. The reason for this practice will soon become apparent as you keep reading this book.

If all of these biased tactics were not enough, one heavily cited paper used yet another tactic of preselection before the research got going to select segments of chimp DNA for sequencing in chimp chromosome number 22.[10] The cherry-picking was done using human DNA markers to locate the most human-like regions on chimp chromosome 22. Once again, we have an initial level of biased preselection to weed out chimp DNA that is not similar to human and find the segments that are the most similar. In this case, it's being employed before the DNA sequence is even produced. But it gets worse because the researchers also knew that human and chimp chromosomes 22 were well known at that time to be the most similar to each other compared to the rest of the genome.[11] As I continued to evaluate the research paper, it also became apparent that critical overall DNA alignment statistics were not given. The authors indicated a level of single nucleotide differences of 1.44% in the aligned human and chimp DNA segments,

> "Another major problem with this effort was the fact that the chimp DNA sequences were stitched together using the human genome as a scaffold or guide, effectively humanizing it."

but important similarity information is also contained in the stretches of DNA that are different, called gaps. While they do indicate that there were 82,000 gaps and provided a simple graph showing their size distribution, no information for average gap size or total length of the gaps was given. At every level of this study, even with the reporting of the results, the data were cherry-picked to promote the most favorable evolutionary outcome and bolster the 98.5% similarity gold standard. Interestingly, based on an estimate using numbers from the limited graphical data that were presented, an estimate of about 80% overall similarity can be readily obtained for this study when the gaps are added back in.

The Chimp Genome First Draft

The high-water mark for human-chimp DNA comparison was the 2005 paper from the International Chimpanzee Genome Sequencing Consortium.[12] Like its predecessors, this effort followed the established paradigm where the data presented were highly selective and large amounts of nonsimilar DNA data were not well accounted for. Another major problem with this effort was the fact that the chimp DNA sequences were stitched together using the human genome as a scaffold or guide, effectively humanizing it. In addition, an extensive analysis done of the raw DNA sequence data sets used in the project years later revealed that they were likely heavily contaminated with human DNA, a common problem in many genome projects of that era that has been well documented. More on the contamination issue will be discussed below.

One thing that was noteworthy in the chimp genome paper was that detailed data regarding the overall actual genome-wide DNA similarity between chimps and humans as a grand summary were conspicuously absent. Despite this lack of an estimate for total genome similarity, proponents of the human evolution story often cite this paper as strong evidence for nearly identical DNA similarity between humans and chimps. In fact, true to protocol, the standard practice of cherry-picking was employed in the data summary. The majority of the research was concentrated on hypothetical evolutionary analyses of highly similar regions for theoretical and speculative things like divergence rates and selective forces. This was a very effective way to sidestep the fact that overall the human and chimp genomes were not nearly as similar as the previous years of popular propaganda had so authoritatively proclaimed.

So what about the big question of overall genome similarity? As it turns out, one

can actually figure this out based on a variety of statistics given in the paper and the known amount of assembled human sequence from the human genome project at that time.[1] In the chimp genome paper, the authors say, "Best reciprocal nucleotide-level alignments of the chimpanzee and human genomes cover ~2.4 gigabases (Gb)" and "the indel differences between the genomes thus total ~90 Mb". At this point in time, the human genome was estimated to be nearly complete with about 2.85 billion bases of total sequence.[13] The key data point is that when we subtract out the nonmatching DNA bases from the 2.4 billion aligned bases, we only get about 2.3 billion that could be aligned onto the human genome at 2.85 billion. A simple percent calculation reveals an overall genome-wide estimate at a very conservative 80.6%. This is a far cry from the 98.5% gold standard adhered to by most researchers up to that point.

High Similarity Due to Contamination?

Another important factor to consider in the human-chimp similarity paradigm is that some of the observed high DNA similarity is due to human DNA contamination. Not only has this occurred accidently in the lab but also on purpose by the insertion of human DNA electronically as stated by researchers themselves.

First, let's start with contamination of an accidental nature. Not only is the chimp genome assembly (construction) still largely based on the human genome as a framework, my own published research analyzing the raw DNA sequences that went into constructing it is shocking. The first generation of raw DNA sequence data sets that produced the 2005 rough draft of the chimp were on average 6% more identical to human than the same type of sequences produced later in the project after the paper was published. How can this be explained? As it turns out, the problem of human DNA contamination in public DNA databases produced during the early era of the chimp genome project is a valid concern. In 2011, a scientifically disturbing study was published in which researchers evaluated 2,749 non-primate public databases and discovered that 492 were contaminated with human DNA at levels of up to 10%.[14] The contaminated databases included species of bacteria, plants, and fish. Ape and monkey databases were not evaluated, leaving the question open as to how much human DNA contamination may be present in ape genomes. More recently in 2016, another study was published in which the occurrence of contaminating human DNA was found to persist. The authors of this paper stated, "We recommend that existing contaminated genomes should be revised to remove contaminated sequence, and that new assemblies should be thoroughly checked for presence of human DNA before submitting them to public databases."[15]

We now know that human DNA contamination is a result of the vulnerable process of working in an open lab where airborne human cells get into samples from coughing, sneezing, and contaminated fingers. Compounding the problem is the fact that the detection of human DNA contamination in ape and even other mammal databases can be a difficult and highly subjective task because some regions of the genome are very similar between humans and other mammals. It's important to note that the chimpanzee genome was sequenced during this time period where widespread human DNA contamination was common and not well understood.

The laboratory contamination problem is compounded by the use of human DNA sequence to assemble and characterize (annotate) chimp DNA based on the evolutionary assumption of shared common ancestry and, of course, the 98.5% gold standard. In fact, this electronic version of DNA contamination was actually introduced intentionally during the assembly and annotation of the chimp genome in all published versions through PanTro4. On a 2013 web page at one of the world's leading DNA sequence databases (www.ensembl.org), the page titled "Chimp Genebuild" gave the following enlightening information.

Owing to the small number of proteins (many of which aligned in the same location) an additional layer of gene structures was added by projection of human genes. The high-quality annotation of the human genome and the high degree of similarity between the human and chimpanzee genomes enables us to identify genes in chimpanzee by transfer of human genes to the corresponding location in chimp.[16]

And...

The protein-coding transcripts of the human gene structures are projected through the WGA (whole genome assembly) onto the chromosomes in the chimp genome. Small insertions/deletions that disrupt the reading-frame of the resultant transcripts are corrected for by inserting "frame-shift" introns into the structure.[16]

> "The percentage of nucleotides in the human genome that had one-to-one exact matches in the chimpanzee genome was 84.38%."

What an amazing revelation quoted directly from the group responsible for producing the chimp genome! These people actually added human gene sequence to the chimp DNA that did not exist and even "corrected" insertions and deletions to make the sequence more human-like.

2018 Chimp Genome Derails Evolution

Since the original first draft of the chimp genome, several more have been produced, but the new DNA sequence that is obtained has always been aligned onto the human genome as a scaffold, maintaining its evolutionary bias. In 2018, the chimpanzee genome community finally realized that this was a major problem and created a new version that they claimed was assembled on its own merits—known as a de novo assembly.[17] In this important paper, they state, "The higher-quality human genome assemblies have often been used to guide the final stages of nonhuman genome projects, including the order and orientation of sequence contigs and, perhaps more importantly, the annotation of genes" and "this bias has effectively "humanized" other ape genome assemblies."[17] In huge contrast to the 2005 chimp genome paper, the hypothetical evolutionary analyses were glaringly absent. Perhaps the dehumanizing of the chimp genome made these calculations considerably more difficult.

University of London evolutionary geneticist Richard Buggs immediately took the issue of human-chimp DNA similarity to task shortly after data from the 2018 paper were posted online with some amazing anti-evolutionary results.[18] Buggs reported, "The percentage of nucleotides in the human genome that had one-to-one exact matches in the chimpanzee genome was 84.38%" and "6.29% had no alignment to the chimp assembly." And as we will see in a later chapter describing my own projects using different algorithms and methodologies, the numbers that Buggs came up with on the new chimp genome are very similar to my research.

Human and Chimp DNA Not Nearly Identical

Nearly all the comparative research studies on human-chimp DNA similarity have discarded significant amounts of DNA that do not align or represent gaps in the sequence to achieve a predetermined goal of 98.5%. These evolutionary biases have extended into the construction of the chimpanzee genome that is nothing more than a cleverly humanized version to support the myth of human evolution. Even the evolutionists have come to admit this in recent research reports related to the chimpanzee genome project.

Sadly, most research papers in human-chimpanzee DNA comparisons do not even include enough data to allow a critical researcher the ability to factor in how much original dissimilarity existed before the final highly cherry-picked numbers are given. In other words, the cherry-picking in many of these studies has gone on at every level of the experiment from start to finish.

In regard to an actual estimate of human-chimp DNA similarity from secular data provided (but often buried) in published research, it's safe to say that it's conservatively not more than about 81 to 86%. These numbers actually line up well with several research projects I have published in recent years to analyze huge amounts of chimpanzee DNA sequence for myself, which I will discuss in the next chapter.

Evolutionists are desperate to try and prove that humans are not more than a few base pairs from a chimp because they need a 98 to 99% DNA similarity between humans and chimps to make evolution seem possible within the time frame of three to six million years since we supposedly shared a common ancestor with chimps. Once again, science is on the side of the Bible and unsupportive of the man-made concocted myth of evolutionary theory. The reality is that humans are not apes, have never been apes, but were created separately and uniquely in the image of God as stated in the scriptures of Genesis—the DNA evidence vindicates this.

References

1. Tomkins, J. and J. Bergman. 2012. Genomic monkey business—estimates of nearly identical human-chimp DNA similarity revaluated using omitted data. *Journal of Creation.* 26: 94-100.

2. Bergman, J. and J. Tomkins. 2012. Is the human genome nearly identical to chimpanzee? a reassessment of the literature. *Journal of Creation.* 26: 54-60.

3. Britten, R. J. 2002. Divergence between samples of chimpanzee and human DNA sequences is 5% counting indels. *Proceedings of the National Academy of Sciences.* 99: 13633-13635.

4. Ebersberger, I. et al. 2002. Genomewide comparison of DNA sequences between humans and chimpanzees. *American Journal of Human Genetics.* 70: 1490-1497.

5. Liu, G. et al. 2003. Analysis of primate genomic variation reveals a repeat-driven expansion of the human genome. *Genome Research.* 13: 358-368.

6. Wells, J. 2011. *The Myth of Junk DNA*. Seattle, WA: Discovery Institute Press.

7. Wildman, D. E. et al. 2003. Implications of natural selection in shaping 99.4% nonsynonymous DNA identity between humans and chimpanzees: enlarging genus homo. *Proceedings of the National Academy of Sciences.* 100: 7181-7188.

8. Sakharkar, M. K. et al. 2004. Distributions of exons and introns in the human genome. *Silico Biology.* 4 (4): 387-393.

9. Nielson R. et al. 2005. A scan for positively selected genes in the genomes of humans and chimpanzees. *PLoS Biology.* 3 (6): e170.

10. Watanabe, A. F. et al. 2004. DNA sequence and comparative analysis of chimpanzee chromosome 22. *Nature.* 429: 382-388.

12. The Chimpanzee Sequencing and Analysis Consortium. 2005. Initial sequence of the chimpanzee genome and comparison with the human genome. *Nature.* 437: 69-87.

13. International Human Genome Sequencing Consortium. 2004. Finishing the euchromatic sequence of the human genome. *Nature.* 431: 931–945.

14. Longo, M. S. et al. 2011. Abundant human DNA contamination identified in non-primate genome databases. *PLoS ONE.* 6 (2): e16410.

15. Kryukov, K. and T. Imanishi. 2016. Human Contamination in Public Genome Assemblies. *PLoS ONE.* 11 (9): e0162424.

16. Chimp (Pan troglodytes) Chimp Genebuild Ensembl release 50 - July 2008. Former URL ensembl.fugusg.org/Pan_troglodytes/chimp_build, accessed February 6, 2013. Archive PDF copy available on request, jtomkins@icr.org.

17. Kronenberg, Z. N. et al. 2018. High-resolution comparative analysis of great ape genomes. *Science.* 360 (6393): eaar6343.

18. Buggs, R. How similar are human and chimpanzee genomes? Posted on richardbuggs.com July 14, 2018, accessed August 9, 2018.

3 A More Accurate Estimate of Human-Chimp DNA Similarity

Summary: Since evolutionary studies in the comparison of human and chimpanzee DNA used cherry-picking techniques, this author has conducted his own research. My work has shown that previous studies contained a significant amount of human DNA contamination along with biases introduced by using the human genome as a framework to assemble the chimpanzee DNA sequence. Based on recent uncontaminated chimpanzee DNA sequence, it has been determined that the human and chimpanzee genomes are no more than 84% similar.

Outside of the various human-chimp DNA comparison studies I discussed in the previous chapter, comprehensive and objective comparisons without the practice of cherry-picking the data have been lacking. However, there have been several studies published outside the evolutionist-controlled literature that have given a much more realistic view. In this chapter, we will take a look at data and results from my own research and also show how these results are matching up with data from a new generation of DNA sequencing.

Looking at Raw Chimp DNA Sequence

Over the past 30 years, a variety of different chemistries have been responsible for generating individual small snippets of DNA sequence called reads. These various technologies yielded DNA snippets ranging in length from about 100 to 1,500 bases. Considering the fact that the chimpanzee genome is about three billion bases or letters, it has been a challenging task to assemble these short reads into large contiguous

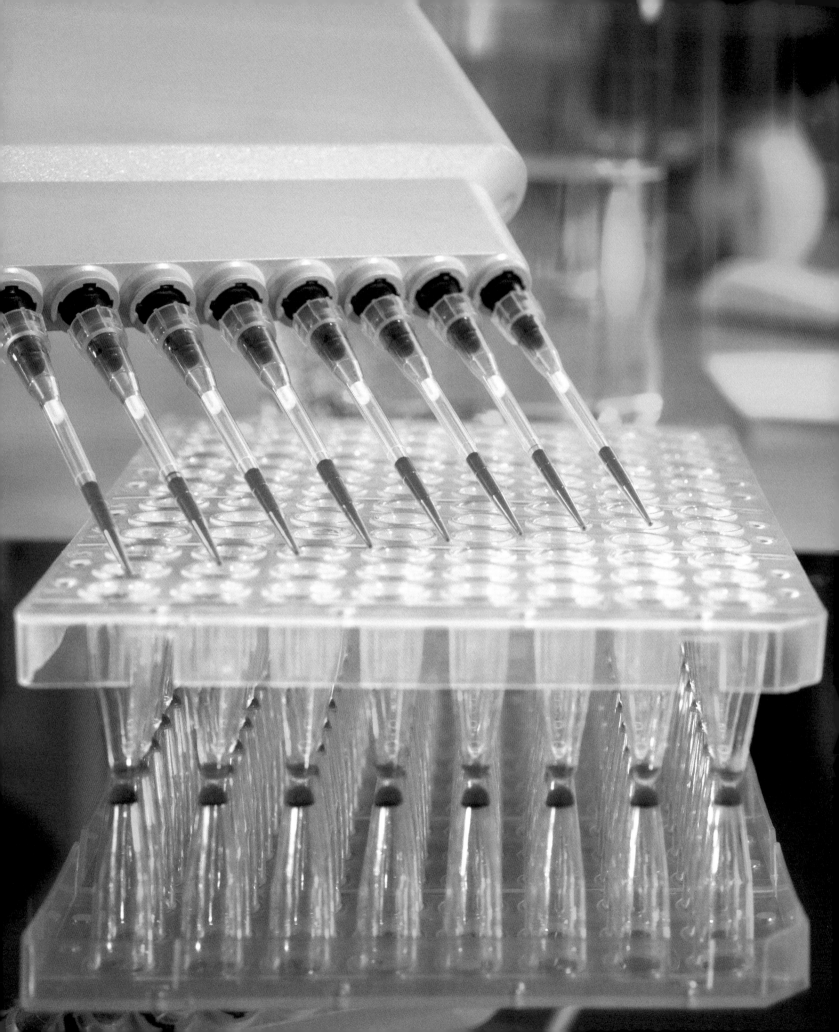

chunks that accurately represent pieces of chromosomes. The challenge is even more formidable when research funding is limited and a good genetic framework to assemble the DNA snippets is lacking, as has been the case for the chimpanzee genome project. As I discussed previously, given the lack of resources combined with a strong evolutionary bias that humans evolved from a chimp-like ancestor, scientists used the human genome as a guide or scaffold.[1]

DNA sequencing has greatly advanced over the past 30 years, and, as in any human endeavor, you have to make improvements to a process based on past mistakes. Not long ago, it became apparent that human DNA contamination from laboratory workers was making its way into many DNA sequencing projects, as discussed in the previous chapter.

A biased method of chimpanzee genome assembly combined with the potential of human DNA contamination produced a flawed chimp genome that would appear to be far more human-like than it actually is. Therefore, I completed and published a research project investigating this issue.[2] My research involved the analysis of over 2.5 million raw chimpanzee DNA sequences from 101 different DNA sequencing data sets that I then compared to both the human genome and the current version of the chimp genome.

When comparing the chimp sequences to human, the analysis indicated that two distinct groups of data sets existed. Those completed early in the chimpanzee genome project (2002 to 2004) were the ones that contributed to the initial version and publication of the chimp genome and were considerably more similar to human than those produced later in the project (2005 to 2011) by a difference of about 7% in overall data set similarity. Amazingly, the DNA sequences from later in the project also produced 6% fewer matches with the human genome. These results imply that early efforts in the chimp genome project contained higher levels of human DNA contamination during a period of time in which the contamination problem in genome sequencing projects wasn't well recognized. Human DNA contamination would also contribute greatly to the assembly of a chimpanzee genome that was much more human-like.

An analysis of the seemingly less-contaminated data sets indicate that the chimpanzee DNA sequences are no more than 85% identical overall to human. When the chimpanzee DNA sequences that did not have matches with the human genome were compared to the chimpanzee genome, the matched regions were very short and full of unexplainable gaps.

If the current chimpanzee genome were an accurate representation, these chimp DNA sequences should have been matching up on the chimp genome at a level of 99.9% similarity. These results clearly show that many regions of the chimp genome are misassembled and therefore can't be used to support human evolution.

Separate Studies Converge on Human-Chimp DNA Dissimilarity

The improving field of DNA sequencing technology, along with scientific advances in the field of genomics, is proving to be a profound testimony against the hypothetical claims of evolution. Two recent discoveries that radically challenge the human evolution paradigm were reported almost simultaneously—one by a secular scientist and the other by myself. And quite remarkably, the corroborating results given in both reports are in perfect agreement with each other.

As mentioned earlier in this book, the newest version of the chimpanzee genome was published in 2018, and the results not only validated the past research I published in 2016 discussed above but also spectacularly confirmed research I published in 2018.[3] First, let's discuss the secular research paper for the newest version of the chimp genome.[4] In this report, researchers describe how they were able to utilize a new long-read DNA sequencing technology to put together the first complete version of the chimp genome based on its own merits without using the human genome as a scaffold. However, this research report documenting the most accurate version of the chimp genome to date completely sidestepped the all-important evolutionary issue of DNA similarity with humans.[4] Despite being neglected in the 2018 chimp genome publication, University of London evolutionist Richard Buggs took it upon himself to analyze the results of a comprehensive comparison of the new chimp genome with human that was posted on a public genomics database. Buggs publicly published his surprising anti-evolutionary findings on the internet, much to the shock of the academic world. He stated, "The percentage of nucleotides in the human genome that had one-to-one exact matches in the chimpanzee genome was 84.38%."[5] What makes Buggs' assessment more amazing is the fact that my own published research using an alternative approach and a different algorithm gave nearly identical results. In my study, I aligned 18,000 random pieces of high-quality chimp DNA that were each on average 30,544

DNA letters long onto the human genome and several different versions of the chimp genome. My analysis showed that the aligned segments of chimp DNA were on average only 84.4% identical to human, the same level of similarity reported by Buggs.

Another interesting discovery I made was that the 30,544 base chunks of chimp DNA were unable to contiguously align onto human in their entirety before the algorithm broke off the match due to nonsimilarity. On average, only about 10,508 bases of each piece of DNA (about one third) could be matched before the DNA sequence became too dissimilar. In other words, the 84% identity that I was able to achieve appears to be an upper limit for DNA similarity, and the actual amount of overall similarity between human and chimpanzee DNA is most likely much lower.

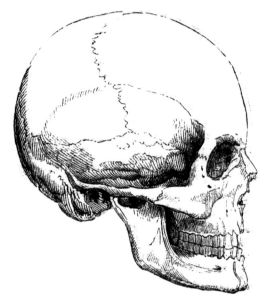

114.—Human Skull.

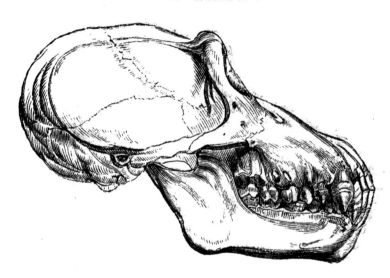

116.—Skull of Chimpanzee.

Another very important fact I discovered is that the older version of the chimp genome known as PanTro4 was deeply flawed and humanized. The 30,544 letter chunks of chimp DNA matched perfectly onto the new highly accurate version of the chimp genome at close to 100% identity for their full length, but when I aligned them onto the previous PanTro4 version of the chimp genome, the poor alignment results were almost similar to that achieved using human. Shockingly, the average identity for the matches was only 91% and the average length of the alignments was 10,699 letters long. In the new PanTro6 version of the chimp genome, the researchers admitted that previous versions of the chimp genome were "humanized." My research confirmed this inconvenient truth, but sadly the PanTro4 humanized version of the chimp genome is still being used as the default chimp genome for research and comparison to human despite its clear evolutionary bias and deeply flawed nature.

Putting the Research Pieces Together

A key element of the human evolution myth is the belief that human and chimp DNA is 98.5% identical. This level of DNA similarity is an important component of the speculation that humans and chimps shared a common ancestor three to six million years ago. Based on known DNA mutation rates observed in humans and chimps, levels significantly lower than 98.5% similarity would destroy the genetic foundation of the entire paradigm.

When I began researching the scientific literature on the subject, I soon realized there were serious discrepancies with the evolutionary concept of nearly identical human and chimp DNA. In every publication I examined, it became obvious that researchers had cherry-picked nearly identical DNA sequences that undergirded evolution and discarded or avoided data that were dissimilar.[6] Where it was possible to determine, I recalculated DNA similarities by factoring back in data that had been omitted and achieved markedly lower levels of human-chimp DNA similarity between 66% and 86%.

After a long quest of examining huge amounts of DNA sequence data myself, in 2016 I published an important comprehensive study of raw unassembled chimp DNA sequences that revealed that the overall DNA similarity between humans and chimps was no more than 85%. In a follow-up study two years later using longer highly accurate assembled chimp DNA sequences, this number was confirmed and refined to about an 84% similarity between the two genomes.

As things stand now, a 16% minimum disparity in the overall DNA similarity between humans and chimps is a discrepancy that cannot be ignored when no greater than a 1% difference is needed to make humans evolving from an ape-like ancestor seem remotely plausible. This hard fact vindicates the scientific accuracy of the Bible that unequivocally proclaims the uniqueness of humans as stated in Genesis 1:27: "So God created man in His own image; in the image of God He created him; male and

> "As things stand now, a 16% minimum disparity in the overall DNA similarity between humans and chimps is a discrepancy that cannot be ignored when no greater than a 1% difference is needed to make humans evolving from an ape-like ancestor seem remotely plausible."

female He created them." The Bible also clearly states that all creatures reproduce "after their kind." While there is variability within kinds, discontinuity is both biblical and a scientific fact.

On the other hand, some people might say, "Why is there only a 16% difference? That doesn't sound like much." The fact of the matter is that humans and chimps do share many localized protein-coding regions of high to moderate DNA sequence similarity. Common code is serving a similar biochemical purpose whether it be in humans, chimps, or even rabbits. Just as human software developers utilize similar code between software programs, the Creator has also used similar code to achieve similar function across the spectrum of life. This is a standard feature and hallmark of design and engineering. In other words, we should expect both similarity and discontinuity in the DNA of humans, apes, and other animals.

However, the main point we need to make in regard to debunking the lie of human evolution is the fact that overall there is extreme DNA sequence discontinuity between humans and chimps that evolution cannot explain or account for. The sheer magnitude of the DNA sequence discontinuity chasm utterly befuddles the mythical evolutionary timescales and dogmatic presuppositions about a human-chimp common ancestor.

References

1. Tomkins, J. 2011. How genomes are sequenced and why it matters: implications for studies in comparative genomics of humans and chimpanzees. *Answers Research Journal.* 4: 81-88.

2. Tomkins, J. 2016. Analysis of 101 Chimpanzee Trace Read Data Sets: Assessment of Their Overall Similarity to Human and Possible Contamination With Human DNA. *Answers Research Journal.* 9: 294-298.

3. Tomkins, J. 2018. Comparison of 18,000 De Novo Assembled Chimpanzee Contigs to the Human Genome Yields Average BLASTN Alignment Identities of 84%. *Answers Research Journal.* 11: 215-219.

4. Kronenberg, Z. N. et al. 2018. High-resolution comparative analysis of great ape genomes. *Science.* 360 (6393): eaar6343.

5. Buggs, R. How similar are human and chimpanzee genomes? Posted on richardbuggs.com July 14, 2018, accessed August 9, 2018.

6. Tomkins, J. and J. Bergman. 2012. Genomic monkey business—estimates of nearly identical human-chimp DNA similarity re-evaluated using omitted data. *Journal of Creation.* 26 (1): 94-100.

4 Chromosome Fusion Debunked

Summary: Humans have 46 chromosomes while apes have 48. Evolutionists claim this discrepancy can be explained by the end-to-end fusion of two small chromosomes called 2A and 2B in an ape-like ancestor humans shared with chimpanzees. It's also claimed that a fusion-like signature of this event along with an extra fossil centromere is present on human chromosome 2 as proof.

However, both the alleged fusion and centromere sites fail the test when analyzed closely. Not only are these alleged evolutionary signatures very small in size and muddled (degenerate), but both of them are found inside functional genes. The alleged fusion site functions as a genetic switch called a promoter inside a long noncoding RNA gene, and the so-called fossil centromere contains both coding and noncoding sequence inside a large protein-coding gene. Combined together, these data destroy the evolutionary hypothesis of fusion.

How the Fusion Story Got Going

One of the top arguments for humans supposedly having evolved from apes is known as the chromosome fusion theory. The general impetus for this idea is the evolutionary problem that apes have an extra pair of chromosomes compared to humans. Humans have a complement of 46 chromosomes (one set of 23 from the mother and one set of 23 from the father) while apes have 48. If humans evolved from an ape-like creature only three to six million years ago—a mere blip in the grand scheme of the evolution of life on Earth that occurred over an alleged 3.8 billion years since the first cells spontaneously evolved—then why do humans and apes have different numbers of chromosomes? This evolutionary idea to solve the chromosome difference conundrum between apes and humans proposes that an end-to-end fusion of two small ape-like chromosomes (named 2A and 2B) produced human chromosome 2. For a visual illustration of the hypothetical fusion scenario, see Figure 1.

The original idea for the chromosome fusion was based on shared patterns of bands observed using light microscopy for chemically stained chromosomes.[1] This technique uses cells with highly condensed chromosomes that have been isolated during cell division (mitosis), which are then stained with dyes that bind to the DNA and produce patterns of dark and light bands. The name for this technique, which can also be used for detecting diseases associated with major chromosomal aberrations like Down syndrome, is called karyotyping. When this was done with chimp cells, several small chromosomes shared a number of bands similar to human chromosome 2 and were then determined to have fused together end-to-end to form human chromosome 2. Of course, there were a variety of bands not shared between the human and chimp chromosomes as well. In fact, an entire chunk of one of the chimp chromosomes is missing and not even represented in the alleged fusion. Based on a comparative analysis of the karyotypes, this created an extreme size discrepancy or unaccounted-for loss of chimp DNA of about 10% or 24.3 million bases of chimp DNA in the purported fusion (Figure 1). This discrepancy can be calculated based on comparative karyotypes and the known highly accurate DNA sequence size for human chromosome 2.

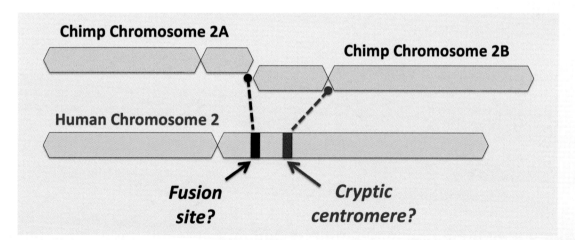

Figure 1. Drawing of the hypothetical model in which chimpanzee chromosomes 2A and 2B fused end to end to form human chromosome 2. The chromosomes were drawn to scale according to cytogenetic images published by Yunis and Prakash.[1] Note the size discrepancy that is about 10% or 24 million bases based on the known size of human chromosome 2.

Another important point to make regarding chromosome banding and comparing karyotypes between humans and chimps is what exactly forms the genetic basis for these banding patterns. Some people have tried to imply that the bands correspond closely to genetic information like genes and have used the false analogy of the bands being chapters in a book, with each book being a chromosome. The basis for these band patterns were not well understood in 1982 when researchers first published their comparative human-chimp karyotypes. We know now that the stained bands are related to the percentages or ratios of the DNA letters C and G to A and T, not specific genes or groups of genes.

The So-Called Fusion Site

The alleged DNA signature of the proposed fusion event between two ape-like chromosomes is located on human chromosome number 2. The particular DNA segment was first isolated and sequenced in 1991, about nine years after the whole fusion idea was first proposed based on the original analysis of comparative karyotypes.[2] Researchers discovered what they thought was the presence of a muddled head-to-head fusion of chromosome end sequences called telomeres (Figure 2). Telomeres are the six-base sequence of DNA letters TTAGG repeated over and over again at the ends

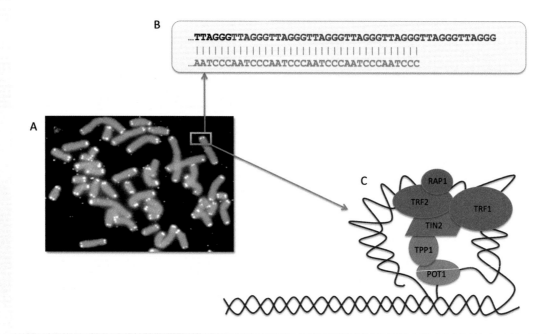

Figure 2. A) Telomeres lit up by a fluorescent probe at the ends of human chromosomes. B) The DNA sequence of the telomeric repeat found at the ends of chromosomes. C) The protein complex called shelterin that shapes and safeguards the telomeres.

of chromosomes. To put it crudely, they act like the plastic sheaths at the ends of shoelaces called aglets that keep them from getting unraveled. The telomere fusion signature discovery was actually somewhat of a surprise to researchers because they were expecting something different based on data from known fusions in living mammals and the apparent loss of a large amount of chimp DNA that was apparent from the karyotype images (Figure 1).

> **"Chromosome fusions representing telomere-telomere DNA signatures like that found at the alleged human fusion site on chromosome 2 have never been found in nature."**

If the alleged telomeric signature was evidence of a true chromosomal end-to-end fusion, then it would actually be the first such case documented in mammals that involved a telomere-to-telomere fusion. This is because all documented known mammalian chromosome fusions in living animals involve a specific type of sequence called satellite DNA (satDNA). This satDNA is found all over the genome, and particularly around areas inside chromosomes called centromeres where some chromosomes can break prior to fusing. The presence of satDNA is a DNA feature that can be involved in breakages and ends up in the subsequent fused chromosome sequence.[3-5] Although chromosome fusions in animals are very rare, in such cases the fusion junction is clearly marked by combinations of telomere-satDNA or satDNA-satDNA, and also often involve centromeres or regions near them. Chromosome fusions representing telomere-telomere DNA signatures like that found at the alleged human fusion site on chromosome 2 have never been found in nature. This absence of documented end-to-end telomere fusions in living animals is due to the fact that telomeres also contain highly specialized end caps of a protein complex that protects them from fusing.[6]

Some evolutionists have tried to counter this argument that telomeres can't fuse together by citing data from the rearranged genomes of human cancer cells. In cancer, cell division is essentially out of control, and all sorts of chromosomal anomalies can be found, including telomere-telomere fusions. But obviously these are not healthy normal cells, and their presence leads to serious life-threatening conditions.

In humans and other mammals, telomeres are composed of the six-base repeat TTAGGG for thousands of bases in length. Healthy human telomeres usually contain 800 to 2,500 of these TTAGGG repeats in perfect tandem.[6] So, in light of the evolutionary fusion story, the main question we must ask when investigating for a signature of telomeric fusion is does the so-called fusion signature contain the hallmarks of an end-to-end fusion of two chromosomes?

When we take a look at the fusion site in detail, it immediately becomes apparent that it is unexpectedly small and only 798 bases in length. This is surprisingly miniscule compared to what should be present if a fusion of two telomeres actually occurred. Even if two of the smallest-size human telomeres fused end-to-end, a DNA sequence of about 10,000 bases in length should exist. If two larger-length telomeres fused, the fusion signature should be about 30,000 bases long.

Not only is the small size a problem for the fusion story, another major discrepancy is that the signature does not really represent a clear-cut fusion of telomeres as is often touted. Even if we assume a very generous evolutionary time frame of six million years since humans split off from a common ancestor with chimps, the muddled

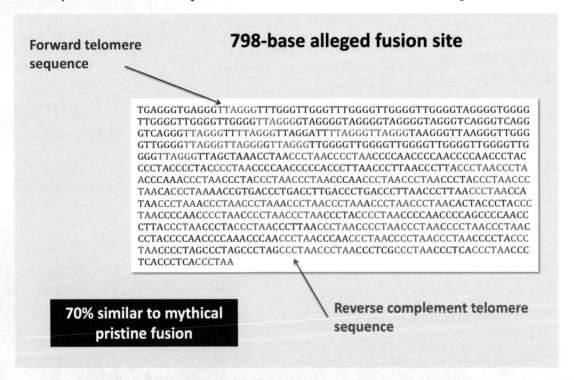

Figure 3. The 798 bp core sequence surrounding the fusion site (highlighted). Intact forward (TTAGGG) and reverse complement (CCCTAA) telomere sequences are also in bold font. Outside this small region, the concentration of telomere sequences totally breaks down, and they are hundreds to thousands of bases apart.

nature of the fusion site sequence does not cooperate. See Figure 3, which shows the DNA letters of the 798 base fusion site with the intact telomere sequences emphasized in bold print.

One of the chief characteristics of the muddled nature of the fusion signature is that there is a marked absence of intact telomeric repeats, and the intact ones that can be found exist independently since they are not present in tandem repeats. Based on predictions for a recent evolutionary fusion, thousands of intact motifs in near-perfect tandem should exist. Within the 798-base fusion signature, only 10 intact TTAGGG telomere sequences exist and only 43 CCCTAA (reverse complement) intact reverse complement telomere sequences are present.

One of the most informative secular research papers on this subject delivered a thorough DNA analysis of the fusion site and over 600,000 bases of DNA surrounding it.[7] In this report, the researchers pointed out that the fusion signature was extremely "degenerate." In evolutionary lingo, this means that it is ambiguous and degraded, and, given its supposed recent evolutionary origin, is a complete surprise. In fact, compared to a fusion signature of the same length that would be composed of perfect pristine repeats, it is only 70% identical. Given the supposed evolutionary time frame, it should be about 98 to 99% identical. Enlightening quotes from the research paper describing this anomalous discovery are below.[7]

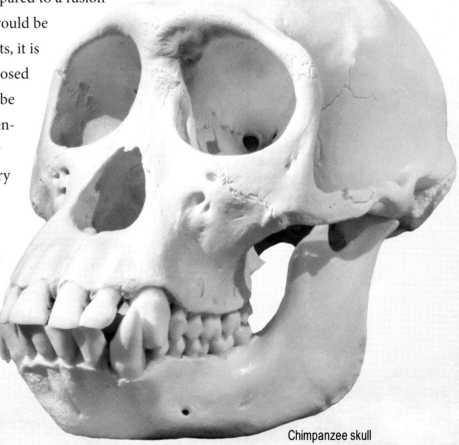

Chimpanzee skull

> Head-to-head arrays of repeats at the fusion site have degenerated significantly from the near perfect arrays of (TTAGGG)n found at telomeres.

> If the fusion occurred within the telomeric

repeat arrays less than ~6 Ma, why are the arrays at the fusion site so degenerate?

So, why is the alleged signature of fusion so small and muddled? Is this an area of the genome with a lot of variability or mutational activity? Actually, just the opposite is the case. The variability in this area based on comparing the genomes of thousands of people around the world indicates that it is about average. In fact, secular researchers have pointed out that areas of the human genome near centromeres, like where the fusion site is located, are generally much more stable and less variable than other parts of the genome. The fusion site itself along with the DNA immediately surrounding it are also void of another class of DNA called transposable elements, which can alter and mutate it. Taken together, this means that any type of mutational mechanism or alteration in the general area of the fusion site is quite low, and that if it was a true hallmark of fusion it should be fairly pristine and not small and degenerate like what we actually see. In reality, the so-called fusion signature is a vague shadow of what should be present if the fusion story were true.

The Fusion Site Inside a Gene?

Despite all of the discrepancies mentioned above, the most remarkable anti-evolutionary discovery about the putative fusion site turned out to be where it was located and what it was actually doing. This whole discovery came during the process of reading the research paper mentioned above that reported a detailed analysis of 614,000 bases of DNA sequence surrounding the alleged fusion site. I noticed in one of the report's figures that the fusion site was potentially located inside a gene (that gene is now called *DDX11L2*) and quite remarkably this oddity was not acknowledged or discussed in the text of the paper.[8] You would immediately think that a finding like this would be highly noteworthy. Perhaps this significant piece of information would have been the nail in the evolutionary coffin, so the researchers refused to discuss it. Needless to say, this major anomaly inspired me to give the fusion site a much closer examination. Because this particular paper had been published in 2002 and I took notice of it in 2013, I knew that a huge amount of data on the structure and function of the human genome had been published since 2002, and there was most likely much more to the story that needed to be uncovered.

When I performed further research, I did in fact verify that the fusion site is

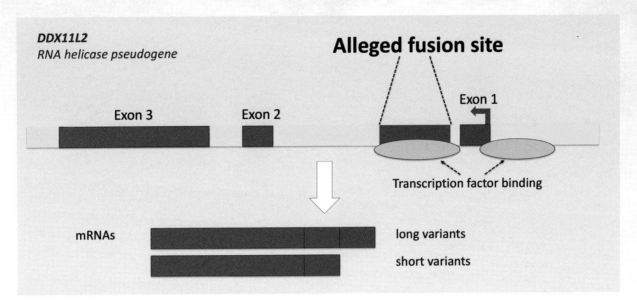

Figure 4. Simplified illustration of the alleged fusion site inside the second intron of the *DDX11L2* gene. The graphic also shows two versions of short and long transcript variants produced along with areas of transcription factor binding. The arrow in the first exon depicts the direction of transcription.

positioned inside a gene, although the name of the gene had changed and is now called *DDX11L2*. Most genes in plants and animals have their coding segments in pieces called exons so that they can be alternatively spliced. Based on the addition or exclusion of exons, genes can produce a variety of products. The intervening regions between exons are called introns, which often contain a variety of regulatory signals and switches that control the function of the gene. The alleged fusion site is positioned inside the first intron of a functional RNA helicase gene called *DDX11L2* (Figure 4).[9]

The DNA molecule is double-stranded with what is called a plus strand and a minus strand. It was engineered this way to maximize information density while also increasing efficiency and function. As a result, there are genes running in different directions on the opposing strands. As it turns out, the *DDX11L2* gene is encoded on the minus strand. The *DDX11L2* gene has three exons, and amazingly the so-called fusion site serves a special purpose. Because genes in humans are like Swiss army knives and can produce a variety of RNAs, in the case of the *DDX11L2* gene it produces short variants consisting of two exons and long variants with three (Figure 4).[9]

So, what might this *DDX11L2* gene be doing? My research showed it is expressed in at least 255 different cell or tissue types.[9] It is also closely co-expressed (turned on at the same time) with a variety of other genes around the genome and is connected to processes associated with cell signaling in the extracellular matrix and blood cell

> "The location of the so-called fusion sequence inside a functional gene associated with the genetics of a wide variety of cellular processes strongly refutes the idea that it is the accidental byproduct of a head-to-head telomeric fusion. Genes are not formed by catastrophic chromosomal fusions!"

production. The location of the so-called fusion sequence inside a functional gene associated with the genetics of a wide variety of cellular processes strongly refutes the idea that it is the accidental byproduct of a head-to-head telomeric fusion. Genes are not formed by catastrophic chromosomal fusions!

But the data refuting fusion do not stop with the fact that it is located inside a gene. The purported fusion site is itself functional and serves an important engineered purpose. My research showed that the fusion site actually serves as a switch for controlling gene activity. In this respect, a wealth of biochemical data showed that 12 different proteins called transcription factors bound to this segment of the gene. One of the proteins that bind to it is none other than RNA polymerase II, the main enzyme that copies RNA molecules from DNA in a process called transcription. Backing up this important discovery is additional data that I uncovered showing that the actual process of transcription initiates inside the region of the so-called fusion site.

Technically speaking, we would call the activity in the alleged fusion site a promoter region. Promoters are the main switches at the beginning of genes that turn them on and where the RNA polymerase starts to create an RNA. Many genes have alternative promoters like the *DDX11L2* gene inside the gene in the first intron. As mentioned, there are actually two areas of transcription factor binding in the *DDX11L2* gene. The first is in the promoter directly in front of the first exon, and the second is in the first intron corresponding to the fusion site sequence. This dual promoter scenario, along with the fact that the *DDX11L2* gene produces RNAs with two or three exons, indicates that the gene undergoes a process called alternative transcription. Not only is the gene itself complexly controlled, with the alleged fusion sequence playing a role, but even the transcripts produced are very complex. My research also showed that the RNAs themselves contain a wide variety of binding and control sites for a class of small regulatory molecules called microRNAs.[9]

Functional Internal Telomere Sequences Are All Over the Genome

The presence of internally located telomere sequence repeats all over the human genome is a mystery to evolutionists and has been known since the first draft of the human genome in 2001. These seemingly out-of-place telomere repeats have been dubbed interstitial telomeres. The presence of these interstitial telomere sequences presents another challenge for the fusion site idea. It's a fact that very few of the telomere repeats in the fusion site occur in tandem. As noted in Figure 3, the sequence of the 798-base fusion site contains only a few instances where two repeats are actually in tandem, and there are none that have three repeats or more. However, there are many other interstitial telomere sites all over the human genome where the repeats occur in perfect tandem three to 10 times or more.[10-11] Internally located clusters of telomere repeats are more common than is realized and not necessarily indicative of a fusion.

Interestingly, it now appears that interstitial telomeric repeats may be serving some important function in the genome related to gene expression besides their role at the ends of chromosomes. In an extensive study, I identified interstitial telomeric repeats all over the human genome and then intersected their genomic locations with a diversity of data sets containing functional biochemical information for gene activity.[12] I discovered that literally thousands of telomeric repeats across the genome were directly associated with the hallmarks of gene expression. As it turns out, the same type of transcription factor binding and gene activity occurring at the alleged fusion site was occurring genome-wide at numerous other interstitial telomeric repeats. Clearly these DNA features are not the accidents of evolution but purposefully and intelligently designed functional code.

Bogus Cryptic Centromere Inside a Gene Too

Yet another key problem with the fusion model is the lack of viable evidence for a signature of an extra centromere region. Centromeres are sections of chromosomes, often in central locations, that play key roles as an attachment site for cell machinery to pull newly replicated chromosomes apart after they have been replicated during cell division. As depicted in Figure 1, immediately following the alleged head-to-head fusion of two chromosomes there would have existed two centromere sites in the newly formed chimeric chromosome. In such a case, one of the centromeres would be functional while the other would be disabled. The presence of two active centromeres is bad news for chromosomes and would lead to chromosome dysfunction and cell destruction. The fusion event along with the silencing of one centromere would have had to occur in a cell lineage during the production of an egg or a sperm to be heritable.

Interestingly, the evidence for a cryptic centromere on human chromosome 2 is

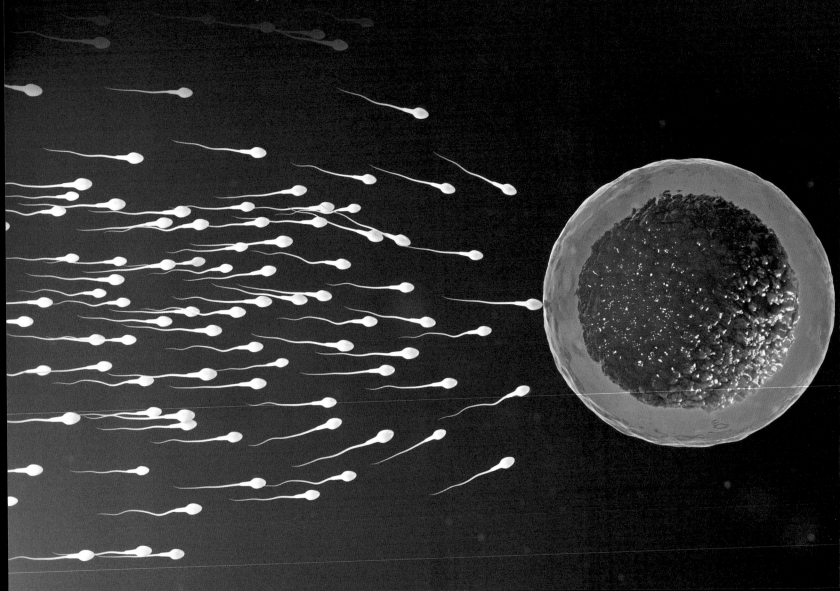

even weaker than that for a telomere-rich fusion site. Evolutionists explain the lack of a clearly distinguishable nonfunctional secondary centromere by arguing that a second centromere would be rapidly selected against. Then, according to the evolutionary model, the disabled centromere would deteriorate over time since there were no functional restraints placed on it any more as doing anything useful in the genome. However, the actual evidence for a second remnant centromere at any stage of sequence degeneration is lacking.

Functional centromere sequences are composed of a repetitive type of DNA called alphoid sequences, with each alphoid repeat being about 171 bases long. There are actually different variations of alphoid sequence across the genome that can be placed into different categories. Some types of alphoid repeats are found all over the genome, while others are specific to centromeres. The structure of the alphoid sequences found at the cryptic centromere site on human chromosome 2 does not match those associated with functional human centromeres.[13] Even worse for the evolutionary overall model is that they have no highly similar counterparts in the chimp genome; they are human specific.[13]

In addition to the evolutionary problem of alphoid repeat structure and nonsimilarity to real centromeres, the alleged fossil centromere is exceptionally tiny compared to a real one. The size of a normal human centromere ranges in length between 250,000 and 5,000,000 bases.[14] However, the alleged cryptic centromere is only 41,608 bases long. It's also important to know that there are three different regions of it that

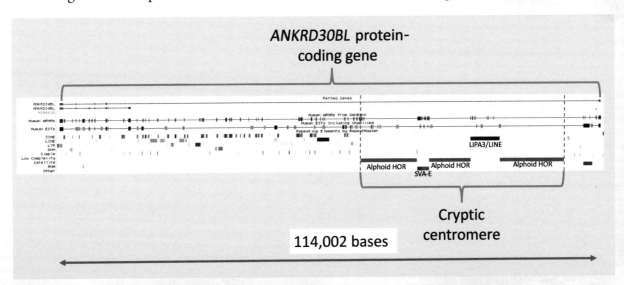

Figure 5. The 41,608-base cryptic centromere region on chromosome 2 that is positioned within the *ANKRD30BL* protein-coding gene

are not even alphoid repeats.[15] Two of these are called retroelements, with one being a LPA3/LINE repeat 5,957 bases long and the other an SVA-E element 2,571 bases long (Figure 5). When we subtract the insertions of these non-alphoid sequences, it gives a length of only 33,080 bases, which is a fraction of the length of a real centromere.

However, the most serious evolutionary problem with the idea of a fossil centromere is that, like the alleged fusion site, it's positioned inside a gene called *ANK-RD30BL* (Ankyrin Repeat Domain 30B Like).[12,15] Intriguingly, the alleged centromere sequence covers both intron and exon regions of the gene. In fact, the part of the alleged fossil centromere sequence that lands inside an exon actually codes for amino acids in the resulting gene's protein (Figure 5). This type of ankyrin repeat protein is associated with the cell's membrane and is believed to be involved in the interaction of the structural network of proteins inside the cell called the cytoskeleton in connection with receptor proteins imbedded in the cell membrane.[16] The fact that the so-called fossil or cryptic centromere is a functional region inside an important protein-coding gene completely refutes the idea that it is a defunct centromere.

Conclusion: No Fusion

Not only are both the alleged fusion and fossil centromere sites highly questionable in their sequence as to being evolutionarily derived from an ancient chromosome fusion due to their muddled signatures and small sizes, they both represent functional sequence inside genes. The alleged fusion site is an important genetic switch called a promoter inside the *DDX11L2* long noncoding RNA gene, and the so-called fossil centromere contains both coding and noncoding sequence inside a large ankyrin repeat protein-coding gene. This is an undeniable double whammy against the whole mythical fusion idea, utterly destroying its validity. The overwhelming conclusion is that the fusion never happened.

References
1. Yunis, J. J. and O. Prakash. 1982. The origin of man: a chromosomal pictorial legacy. *Science*. 215 (4539): 1525-1530.
2. Ijdo, J. W. et al. 1991. Origin of human chromosome 2: An ancestral telomere-telomere fusion. *Proceedings of the National Academy of Sciences*. 88: 9051-9055.
3. Chaves, R. et al. 2003. Molecular cytogenetic analysis and centromeric satellite organization of a novel 8;11 translocation in sheep: a possible intermediate in biarmed chromosome evolution. *Mammalian Genome*. 14 (10): 706-710.
4. Tsipouri, V. et al. 2008. Comparative sequence analyses reveal sites of ancestral chromosomal fusions in the Indian muntjac genome. *Genome Biology*. 9 (10): R155.
5. Adega, F. et al. 2009. Satellite DNA in the karyotype evolution of domestic animals--clinical considerations. *Cytogenetic and Genome Research*. 126 (1-2): 12-20.

6. Tomkins, J. P. and J. Bergman. 2011. Telomeres: implications for aging and evidence for intelligent design. *Journal of Creation.* 25 (1): 86-97.

7. Fan, Y. et al. 2002. Genomic structure and evolution of the ancestral chromosome fusion site in 2q13-2q14.1 and paralogous regions on other human chromosomes. *Genome Research.* 12 (11): 1651-1662.

8. Fan, Y. et al. 2002. Gene content and function of the ancestral chromosome fusion site in human chromosome 2q13-2q14.1 and paralogous regions. *Genome Research.* 12: 1663-1672.

9. Tomkins, J. 2013. Purported Human Chromosome 2 'Fusion Site' Encodes an Active Transcription Factor Binding Domain Inside the Complex and Highly Expressed *DDX11L2* Gene. *Answers Research Journal.* 6: 367-375.

10. Azzalin, C. M. et al. 2001. Human intrachromosomal telomeric-like repeats: sequence organization and mechanisms of origin. *Chromosoma.* 110: 75-82.

11. Ruiz-Herrera, A. et al. 2008. Telomeric Repeats Far From the Ends: Mechanisms of Origin and Role in Evolution. *Cytogenetics and Genome Research.* 122: 219–228.

12. Tomkins, J. P. 2018. Combinatorial genomic data refute the human chromosome 2 evolutionary fusion and build a model of functional design for interstitial telomeric repeats. In *Proceedings of the Eighth International Conference on Creationism.* J. H. Whitmore, ed. Pittsburgh, PA: Creation Science Fellowship, 222-228.

13. Tomkins, J. and J. Bergman. 2011. The Chromosome 2 Fusion Model of Human Evolution - Part 2: Re-Analysis of the Genomic Data. *Journal of Creation.* 25: 111-117.

14. Aldrup-Macdonald, M. E. and B. A. Sullivan. 2014. The Past, Present, and Future of Human Centromere Genomics. *Genes (Basel).* 5 (1): 33-50.

15. Tomkins, J. 2017. Debunking the Debunkers: A Response to Criticism and Obfuscation Regarding Refutation of the Human Chromosome 2 Fusion. *Answers Research Journal.* 10: 45-54.

16. Voronin, D. A. and E. V. Kiseleva. 2008. Functional Role of Proteins Containing Ankyrin Repeats. *Cell and Tissue Biology.* 49 (12): 989–999.

5 The Chimp Y Chromosome Conundrum

Summary: If humans and chimpanzees shared a common evolutionary ancestor millions of years ago, their respective Y chromosomes should be very similar since Y chromosomes are thought to be one of the least evolved, i.e., the least changed, of all chromosomes. But when the chimp Y chromosome was analyzed alongside human, the differences were quite vast, and many portions were unique to either chimp or human.

In fact, the genetic differences between the human and chimp Y chromosomes are so profound that some evolutionists have likened the discrepancy to be the same as comparing human DNA to that of a chicken.

Why Compare Y Chromosomes?

One of the most evolutionary-damaging research reports for the human-chimp similarity paradigm was the high-profile research report on the Y chromosome comparison between chimps and humans.[1] In fact, the differences between the human and chimp Y chromosomes were so large that the scientists in the research paper made the following startling statement.

> The difference in MSY [male specific region] gene content in chimpanzee and human is more comparable to the difference in autosomal gene content in chicken and human, at 310 million years of separation.[1]

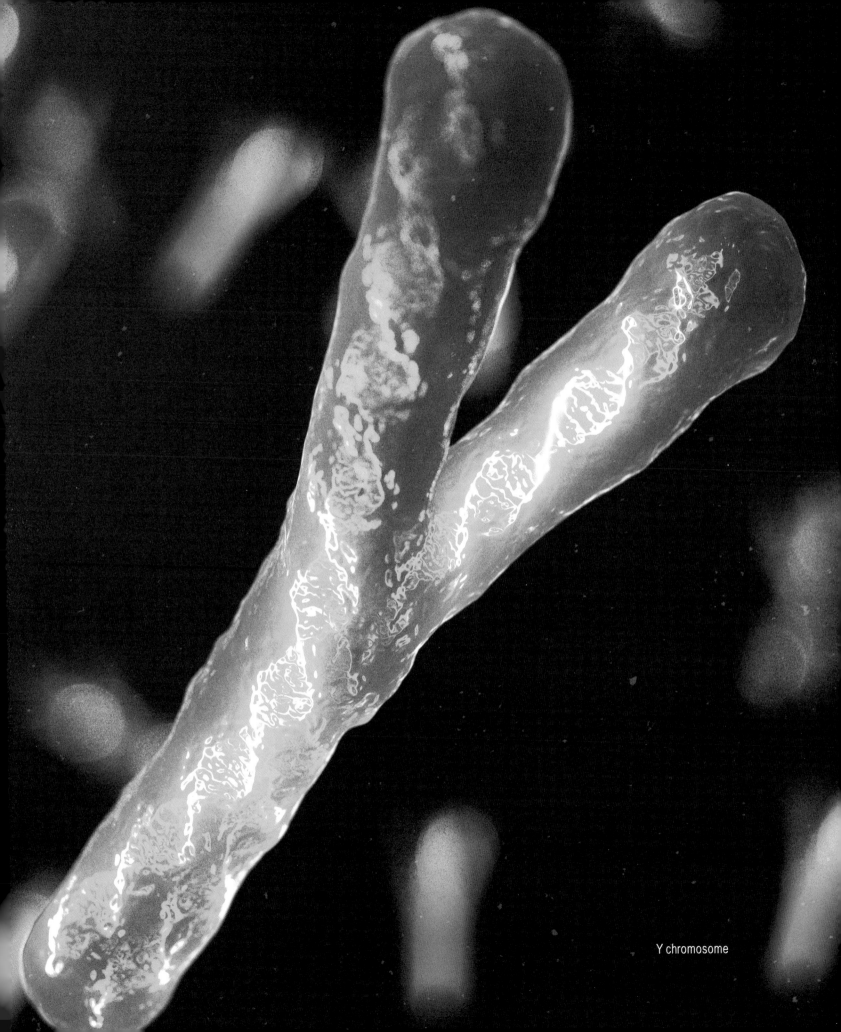

Y chromosome

In other words, the genetic differences between the human and chimp Y chromosomes were so profound that a realistic analogy would be similar to contrasting the amount of differences found when comparing the human and chicken genomes.

One of the chief reasons why evolutionists were highly interested in comparing the Y chromosomes of humans and chimps in great detail was because very little variation is found in the Y chromosome compared to the autosomes (non-sex chromosomes). During the formation of eggs and sperm in a process called meiosis, genetic material is exchanged or shuffled back and forth between similar chromosomes that come from the father and mother. This process is called genetic recombination and very little if any occurs on the Y chromosomes. In other words, it is a very stable chromosome and should be the least evolved or changed since the time of the human-chimp evolutionary split of a common ancestor speculated to have occurred three to six million years ago.

Even though scientists already knew that major size and structural differences existed between the human and chimp Y chromosomes, based on evolutionary reasoning they were anticipating that a gene-rich segment called the MSY region would be nearly identical. The MSY region, or male-specific region of the Y chromosome, differentiates male or female and covers 95% of the chromosome's length. The big shock when comparing the chimp MSY region to human was that they were completely different. In fact, the title of the research paper in the prestigious journal *Nature* was "Chimpanzee and human Y chromosomes are remarkably divergent in structure and gene content."[1]

Exactly What Was Compared?

In this research, the male-specific regions or MSY regions of humans and chimpanzee were compared in detail. This had not been previously possible because the chimp genome was essentially still a rough draft and had been assembled based on the human genome and was not a reliable contiguous representation. For this research, scientists specifically isolated chimp Y chromosome DNA, mapped it out in detail, and then sequenced it in a highly accurate manner. At the time the study was published, this had never been done before for any chimp chromosome.

Because of the new, more complete, and highly accurate chimp Y chromosome sequence, the very large MSY region of the Y chromosome that is largely responsible

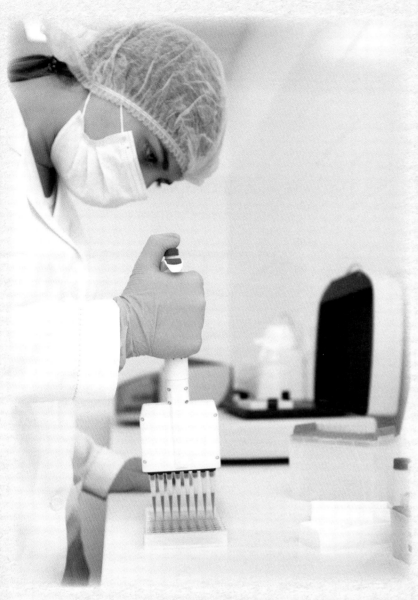

for determining male traits could be analyzed in great detail. Because human and chimp females do not have a Y chromosome, the genes in the MSY region of the Y chromosome trigger development and the ongoing maintenance of male traits. Because the areas of the Y chromosome outside the MSY region are too repetitive and are thought to contain only a few genes, only the MSY regions were compared and contrasted in detail.

When the chimp sequence was compared to the MSY region of the human Y chromosome, the differences were enormous. The researchers state, "About half of the chimpanzee ampliconic sequence has no homologous, alignable counterpart in the human MSY, and vice versa."[1] The ampliconic sequence contains ornate repeat units called palindromes that read the same forward as they do backwards. In humans, the ampliconic regions contain about 60 genes that belong to nine different gene families, and all of them have male-specific function. The ampliconic regions in chimps are difficult to compare since they are structured so radically different from those in humans and have much fewer genes than humans. In fact, when one looks at the overall structure of human compared to chimp for the Y chromosome, it becomes painfully obvious that there is no evolutionary relationship between them that could possibly have arisen over three to six million years of speculated naturalistic processes.

Distributed throughout the entire human MSY region are 27 different families (categorical groupings) of genes, with most being expressed in the male testes. There are nine complete families of genes found on the human Y chromosome that are not even present in chimp (27 versus 18 in human and chimp, respectively). The human

Y also had over twice as many total genes (78 in humans versus 37 in chimp). These huge evolutionary discrepancies were not lost on the authors of this paper, who made the following remarkable statements.

> Despite the elaborate structure of the chimpanzee MSY, its gene reper-
> toire is considerably smaller and simpler than that of the human MSY.[1]

And again…

> The chimpanzee MSY contains only two-thirds as many distinct genes
> or gene families as the human MSY, and only half as many pro-
> tein-coding transcription units.[1]

Besides these distinctively male genes that are only found in humans, there were other areas evaluated that contained genes labeled as X-degenerate, a fairly misleading term based on the assumption that the genes had evolutionary ancestors derived from the female X chromosome. Although the X and Y chromosomes are completely dif-ferent except for a number of small regions, it is believed that in the ancient past the Y evolved from the X. In human females there are two X chromosomes, with one being disabled, while males have both an X and a Y chromosome.

A comparison of the X-degenerate gene regions between chimps and humans revealed profound differences in the order of genes that were similar, the location of genes in the X-degenerate regions, and major differences in overall gene content. In

fact, humans have three categorical types or classes of X-degenerate genes that are not even found in chimp.

Besides the huge differences in gene neighborhood structure and overall gene content between the chimp and human MSY regions, the overall structural differences between the Y chromosomes, as mentioned previously, were enormous. These striking contrasts in overall Y chromosome landscapes between chimp and human involved a number of very enlightening issues regarding the refutation of any evolutionary relationship. These extreme differences are best described by several quotes from the authors of the research publication given below.

> Moreover, the MSY sequences retained in both lineages [human and chimp] have been extraordinarily subject to rearrangement: whole chromosome dot-plot comparison of chimpanzee and human MSYs shows marked differences in gross structure.[1]

> The chimpanzee ampliconic regions are particularly massive (44% larger than in human) and architecturally ornate, with 19 palindromes (compared to eight in human) and elaborate mirroring of nucleotide sequences between the short and long arms of the chromosome, a feature not found in the human MSY.[1]

> Of the 19 chimpanzee palindromes, only 7 are also found in the human MSY; the other 12 are chimpanzee-specific. Unlike the human MSY, nearly all of the chimpanzee MSY palindromes exist in multiple copies.[1]

The huge differences in both the structural arrangement of DNA features unique to chimp and in gene content as described in the Y chromosome study are extremely damaging to the human-chimp DNA similarity myth and the dogma of human evolution from an ape ancestor. In fact, one of the most telling statements made by the scientists who published this study is worth repeating again.

> 6 million years of separation, the difference in MSY gene content in chimpanzee and human is more comparable to the difference in autosomal [non sex chromosomes] gene content in chicken and human, at 310 million years of separation.[1]

Y Chromosomes Debunk Human Evolution

From an evolutionary perspective, the main problem with these drastic differences between the human and chimp Y chromosomes is that the nearly identical DNA similarity dogma required for evolution simply cannot account for it. A global study of genetic variation in the human genome across people groups showed that the Y chromosome was incredibly nonvariable and stable, with five times less genetic variation than the autosomes.[2,3] This genetic variation study examined the DNA sequence from thousands of humans all over the world to see how much variation was present among humans and which chromosomes were the most variable. In the evolutionary paradigm, the chromosomes and the parts of chromosomes that exhibit the most variability are supposedly those that are the most rapidly evolving.

The low levels of variability found on the Y chromosome make perfect sense because it has no similar counterpart in the genome and undergoes very little recombination with the X chromosome during the genetic shuffling process of meiosis in the formation of sperm and egg cells. Humans and most animals have two sets of chromosomes derived from the genetic contributions of mother and father. During the amazing process of meiosis, the various chromosomes line up with their proper maternal and paternal counterparts and exchange DNA segments with each other in a process called recombination. This is why children derived from the same set of parents all look different. Recombination is a cleverly designed and highly controlled mechanism designed by God to facilitate genetic variation and avoid the negative effects of inbreeding. Because the idea of variation is key to evolution, they believe that it's a process that helps facilitate evolution on a grand scale, despite the fact that we don't actually see macroevolution happening either now or in the fossil record. The fact that the Y chromosomes of chimp and humans are so radically different yet are also the least variable chromosomes in the genome completely flies in the face of all evolutionary speculation.

Given this low level of recombination and DNA sequence variability on the Y chromosome, the human evolution model encounters an insurmountable problem— the human and chimp Y chromosomes should be considerably more similar to each other. In fact, if human evolution is true, the chimp and human Y chromosomes should be the most similar to each other in the genome because they are the most stable, having the least variation. However, they are the most different of the chromosomes in the genome between human and chimps. This totally befuddles the evolutionary dogma of human-ape evolution.

> **"**If human evolution is true, the chimp and human Y chromosomes should be the most similar to each other in the genome because they are the most stable, having the least variation. However, they are the most different of the chromosomes in the genome between human and chimps. This totally befuddles the evolutionary dogma of human-ape evolution.**"**

As mentioned above, evolutionists deem increased levels of DNA sequence variability as positive indicators of places in the genome that are supposedly undergoing rapid evolution. Therefore, the Y chromosome should have the signature of rapid evolution hallmarked by DNA sequence variation, but it does not. Instead, the Y chromosome is very static and unchanging. The proven nonvariability of the Y chromosome contrasted to the rest of the human genome, combined with the huge DNA sequence differences between human and chimp, are insurmountable chasms for the human-chimp common ancestry dogma.

The remarkably different DNA sequence of the Y chromosomes between human and chimp presents a very serious problem for common ancestry. In fact, this study in and of itself is powerful evidence against the dogma of human evolution.

References

1. Hughes, J. F. et al. 2010. Chimpanzee and human Y chromosomes are remarkably divergent in structure and gene content. *Nature*. 463: 536-539.
2. Bachtrog, D. 2013. Y-chromosome evolution: emerging insights into processes of Y-chromosome degeneration. *Nature Reviews Genetics*. 14: 113-124.
3. International SNP Map Working Group. 2001. A map of human genome sequence variation containing 1.42 million single nucleotide polymorphisms. *Nature*. 409: 928-933.

6 Human-Specific Genes Defy Evolution

Summary: Most creatures have genes unique to their kind known as orphan genes. Evolutionists have trouble explaining orphan genes since there is no counterpart to them in other creature kinds that would connect them, and because descendants from a common ancestor should inherit similar genes from that ancestor. Random chance processes can't explain orphan genes—it appears they've been engineered to enable various kinds of creatures to thrive in specific environments and are the product of a Designer.

The Orphan Gene Enigma

Most plant, animal, and microbial genomes that are classified as a eukaryotic organism (have a nucleus and cell organelles) contain a large fraction of genes (10 to 20%) that are taxonomically restricted to that particular type of creature.[1] These are called taxonomically restricted genes, or more popularly orphan genes. They are characterized by the simple fact that they lack similar counterparts in other organisms and are specific to that type of creature. Another very intriguing feature is that many orphan genes appear to be related to functional features and adaptations specific to the environmental niches the organism is adapted to.[2-4]

Evolutionary theory is plagued by the problem that orphan genes are nearly impossible to explain because they do not have any genetic ancestors due to the fact that they appear suddenly in the spectrum of life and are unique to a certain type of plant or animal. Evolutionists speculate that most genes have arisen by being copied from other genes and then rearranged and repurposed over long periods of time in a mythical process of tinkering. However, this hypothetical process does not explain orphan genes because they don't have any ancestral sequences from which they could have been derived. Orphan genes appear suddenly, are fully functional, and code for important proteins needed by the organism.[1-4]

Evolutionists say that many orphan genes evolved from noncoding DNA via random mutational processes because they have no other naturalistic explanation to turn to. However, random mutational events are incapable of producing the complex information encoded in genes. There is no valid naturalistic explanation for the appearance of orphan genes.

What Are Orphan Genes?

Technically speaking, orphan genes are expressed gene sequences that code for either a functional RNA molecule or a protein. The categorization of orphan is based on the evolutionarily inconvenient problem that these genes have no similar counterpart in their own genome or in any other organismal genome outside that particular taxon or type of creature. In the scientific literature, orphan genes are now commonly referred to as taxonomically restricted genes, or TRGs. The types of TRGs have different levels of taxonomic specificity. For example, some might be insect-specific, others might be specific to Hymenoptera (bees, wasps, and ants), while others might be only found in a certain kind of ant.[4-5]

Evolutionists believe that the majority of genes have evolved from pre-existing ancestor genes through processes that occur over very long periods of time. The main aspect of this hypothetical process involves the alleged duplication of existing genes over and over again. After they are duplicated, it's believed they are then reshuffled and rearranged to create new

German wasp

genes with new functions. This overall idea is based on the fact that many genes, even within the same genome of an organism, can share regions of similarity. Genes that have significant levels of sequence similarity with each other are typically classified as being members of gene families.

While gene duplication may actually happen on rare occasions, it's not a process that has been empirically documented as being real. In fact, there are a number of serious problems with the gene duplication model as a significantly viable mechanism in evolution. First of all, changing the copy number of most genes, even those within gene families, often causes disease and developmental aberrations that either harm or kill the organism. Secondly, alleged duplicated genes are each integral functional units of highly complex and interdependent gene networks. To think that by copying one of these complex pieces of code, reinserting it in the genome, and then randomly altering bits of it will actually result in something beneficial and complexly integrated is absurd in most cases. I challenge any computer programmer to apply the same strategy to their code and see what they get.

It is now well established that genes function in incredibly complex, hierarchical, interdependent, and exquisitely controlled networks. In addition, gene networks are dynamic and respond to all sorts of cues and signals that are constantly monitored by the cell's systems. There is nothing equivalent to this level of complexity, innovation, and efficiency in the engineered systems devised by the cleverness of mankind.

Theoretical evolutionists would do well to take a lesson from computer programming. Seasoned programmers always reuse parts of their code and syntax in different pieces of their work and between different programs. In fact, all computer languages have a reserved set of key words that are the same no matter what the program is. Other reserved words are related to certain built-in and third-party libraries that are called up during the course of programming. The same engineering principle is found in the genetic code of animal and plant genomes. There are certain genetic words that are conserved at different levels of taxonomic specificity. The observed appearance of gene duplication is simply a standard principal of engineered code.

Related to this concept of gene evolution is the idea of pseudogenes that are thought to be duplicated dysfunctional genes. While not the focus of this chapter, it's sufficient to know that many pseudogenes are being shown to code for functional RNAs involved in gene regulation. See chapter 7 for more information on pseudogenes.

Orphan Genes and Human Evolution

Orphan genes in humans are powerful evidence refuting the idea that we evolved from a common ancestor with chimpanzees. This is because these genes are unique and specific to humans. They show no evidence of a common gene ancestor with apes or any other creature.

Scientists have estimated there are about 24,500 genes in the human genome, and about 20,500 have been associated with functional proteins. In 2013, another 5,737 protein-coding genes were discovered that had somehow been missed previously.[6] This would bring the total number of genes to somewhere between 25,000 and 30,000. Because most genes produce a wide variety of variants and protein products through the amazing ingenuity and utility of the genetic code, this results in more than two million different protein variants being discovered in the human body derived from only about 25,000 genes!

One of the first studies demonstrating dramatic differences between humans and chimps in gene complements was published in 2006. In this report the authors stated, "Our results imply that humans and chimpanzees differ by at least 6% (1,418 of 22,000 genes) in their complement of genes, which stands in stark contrast to the oft-cited 1.5% difference between orthologous nucleotide sequences."[7] A year later in 2007, another report was published in which 1,285 unique genes were found that were specific to the human genome and not found in chimps or any other animal's genome.[8] As mentioned above, another 5,737 protein-coding genes have been added to the human genome, and it's likely that a significant fraction of these will prove to be human-specific.

As human orphan gene research progressed, one study in 2011 reported on 584 genes in humans that were not found in any of the ape species and not part of any known primate gene family.[9] The researchers targeted 60 of the 584 genes for additional study and then determined the human tissues that these were expressed in.

Evolutionists have a keen interest in ascertaining what types of traits and tissues are correlated with the activity of various genes in the hopes of finding those related to evolution in humans. They specifically look for things they think are directly associated with advances in human evolution, like brain genes. Despite the fact that humans and chimps share many anatomical differences, the evolutionary focus seems to be on the brain and why it is larger and how it develops and is organized differently.

As noted above, 60 human-specific genes were targeted for a focused study of their activity throughout the body. Interestingly, they were found to be genetically active in a wide variety of tissues around the human body. These tissues included brain, adipose, breast, heart, colon, liver, skeletal muscle, lymph node, lung, and testes. The highest levels of expression for these human-specific genes were found in the brain and testes. However, it's noteworthy that these genes were shown to be associated with a wide range of activity throughout the body.

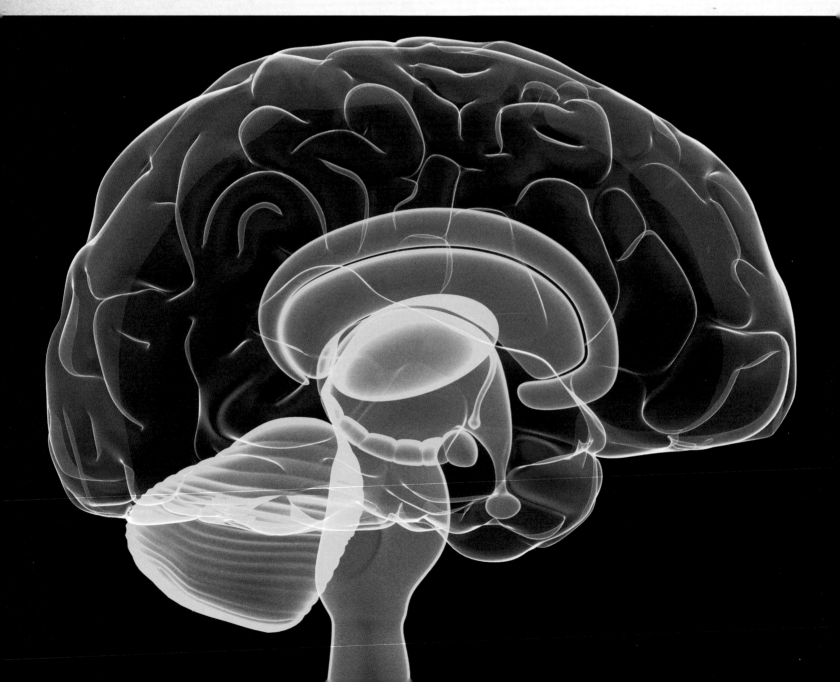

A more recent study in 2015 reported the identification of 634 human-specific genes along with 780 genes that were specific to chimps and not found in humans.[10] Taken together, this is a difference of 1,414 unique genes. If humans evolved from a common ancestor with chimps only three to six million years ago, a blink of the eye in evolutionary time, then how is it that they magically gained 634 unique genes while at the same time not inheriting any of the 780 unique chimp genes? But these gene differences are only for those that are unique and not members of gene families. It's also important to keep in mind that there are many gene differences between human and chimp for those genes that are members of gene families as mentioned above and as also described in the earlier chapter on the Y chromosome differences between humans and chimps.

Role of Orphan Genes

Orphan genes are being demonstrated to have key roles in a variety of complex genetic and biochemical pathways in a variety of creatures across the spectrum of life.[1-4] They have also been linked in their function with other genes in elaborate networks of interdependence and regulatory control. In fact, some of these genes can be lethal to the organism when mutated and disrupted. All of this amazing research begs the question of how these organism-specific genes could appear suddenly and fully integrated into complex networks in the genome without being designed and engineered from the very beginning.

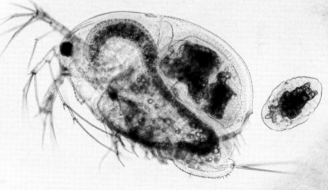

Water flea

Another very intriguing aspect of orphan genes is that they have also been shown to be associated with the unique and specific adaptability of an organism to its environmental niche. As an amazing case in point, the well-studied little animal called the water flea (*Daphnia pulex*) contains many orphan genes that are only expressed under specific sets of environmental conditions and stresses related to water availability. The authors of the paper state, "More than a third of Daphnia's genes have no detectable homologs in any other available proteome."[11] Over 7,000 unique environmentally adaptive genes required by oysters to make shells and to live relatively stationary lives in the environmental complexity of subtidal zones have been identified that have absolutely no evolutionary explanation of origins.[12] Many of these genes confer the amazing ability to deal with extreme variations in temperature, salinity, the concentrations of suspended sediments, and available oxygen. The same case for the discovery of large numbers of environmentally adaptive orphan genes was also discovered for zebrafish that were surprisingly distinct from all the other teleost fishes.[13] In another research paper, the genomes of seven ants, a honeybee, and various solitary insects were examined in which it was found that each ant lineage contained about 4,000 unique genes specific to that type of ant.[4]

Failed Logic of De Novo Gene Synthesis and Orphan Genes

The basic paradigm for orphan genes is due to the fact that they appear suddenly in a type of creature with no evidence of any past evolutionary ancestry. In other words, they have no similar counterparts in the genomes of other taxon. In fact, orphan genes exist at many levels of taxonomic distance, but that is another story for another time. While creature-specific sets of genes make perfect sense within the creation paradigm that affirms God created everything after its kind, evolutionists reject the concept of engineered design in biological systems in complete defiance of the evidence. Therefore, they must come up with some naturalistic account of how these cleverly designed DNA sequences were magically generated in very recent evolutionary time, no matter how illogical the reasoning is.

> **They must come up with some naturalistic account of how these cleverly designed DNA sequences were magically generated in very recent evolutionary time, no matter how illogical the reasoning is.**

The general idea being used to explain the existence of orphan genes involves a completely fictional process devoid of any realistic mechanism called de novo gene synthesis. This is the supposed random, rapid, and magical mutational creation of fully functioning genes from noncoding DNA sequence or massive alterations of protein-coding sequence. It would be like taking a chapter from a book, random mixing up all the letters, and then producing a completely different legible story replete with proper spelling and grammar.

The reasoning, or lack thereof, regarding the magical production of orphan genes is a circular form of standard evolutionary illogic that goes like this. Orphan genes have no ancestral sequences in other creatures that they evolved from. Therefore, they must have evolved rapidly via de novo gene synthesis, and de novo gene synthesis must be true because orphan genes exist…and orphan genes exist because of de novo gene synthesis. This faulty logic is called a circular tautology.

The various research papers that allegedly document de novo gene synthesis are based on nothing but this enigmatic circular reasoning. Unfortunately, much of the academic world operates off of case precedent like the modern judicial system does. Once a court case is settled, even though it may be misjudged it serves as a precedent for future cases. For all practical purposes, this has been the scenario associated with publications surrounding the mythical idea of de novo gene synthesis. Recent publications cite the earlier papers that are based on this circular reasoning as "problem solved," despite the fact they contain no empirical proof whatsoever.

Orphan Genes Negate Human Evolution

Thanks to the wonders of modern genomics, scientists have documented an evolutionarily befuddling category of genes termed orphan genes or taxonomically restricted genes that are specific to each type of organism. Orphan genes identified in humans have been linked to important functions all over the body. More importantly, these genes appear in the human genome suddenly without any trace of prior ancestry in apes or any other animal. They simply don't fit the hypothetical evolutionary paradigm.

A considerably better explanation for the presence of orphan genes can be formulated within the context of specified engineering and the concept of created kinds as described in Genesis. The Bible states 20 different times that creatures reproduce "after their kind." The multitude of different plant and animal kinds were clearly designed with specific genetic boundaries or genomes. Orphan genes are an obvious component of the genomic landscape that is indicative of the specificity of a created kind.

Because orphan genes are specific to each type of creature's genome and also relat-

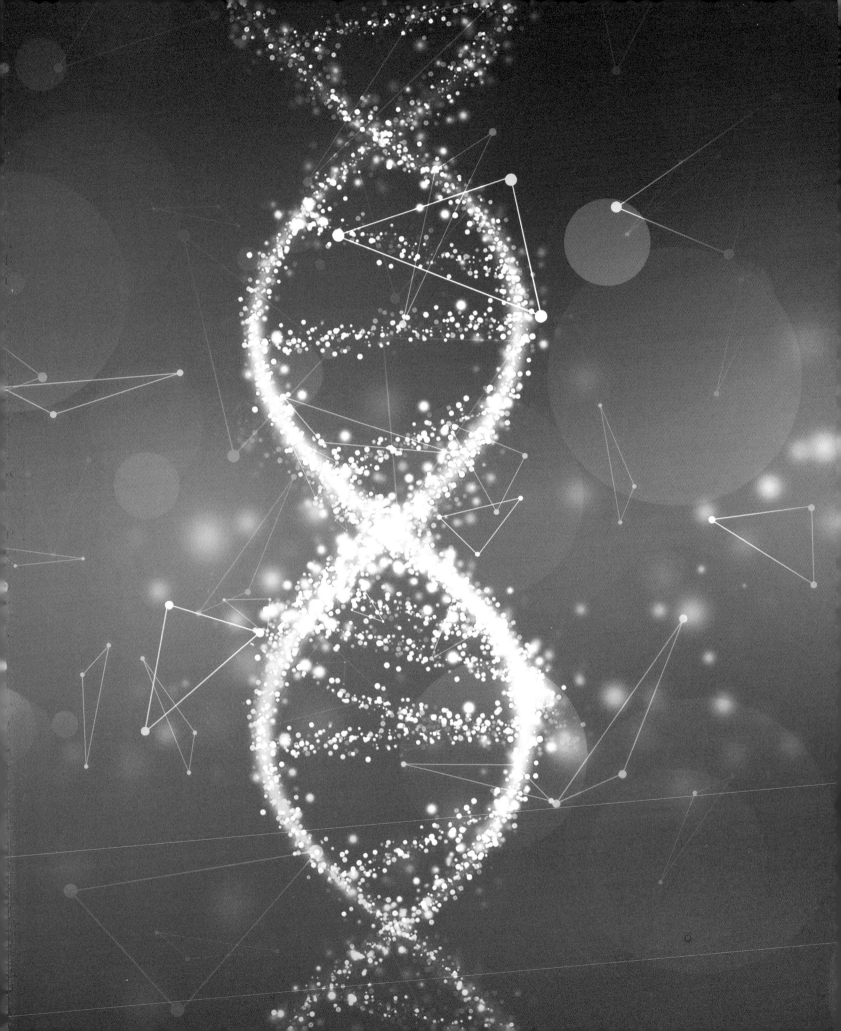

ed to environmental niche adaptation, their existence most closely fits with a biblical model of created kinds. Humans are unquestionably unique among the spectrum of life and, as indicated in the text of Genesis, created in the image of God. The scientific data in this book clearly show that we are not evolved from apes.

References

1. Khalturin, K. et al. 2009. More than just orphans: are taxonomically-restricted genes important in evolution? *Trends in Genetics*. 25 (9): 404-413.

2. Tautz, D. and T. Domazet-Loso. 2011. The evolutionary origin of orphan genes. *Nature Reviews Genetics*. 12: 692-702.

3. Nelson, P. A. and R. J. A. Buggs. 2016. Next generation apomorphy: The ubiquity of taxonomically restricted genes. In P. Olson, J. Hughes, and J. Cotton, eds. *Next Generation Systematics*. Systematics Association Special Volume Series, Cambridge: Cambridge University Press, 237-263.

4. Simola, D. F. et al. 2013. Social insect genomes exhibit dramatic evolution in gene composition and regulation while preserving regulatory features linked to sociality. *Genome Research*. 23 (8): 1235-1247.

5. Johnson, B. R. 2018. Taxonomically Restricted Genes Are Fundamental to Biology and Evolution. *Frontiers in Genetics*. 9: 407.

6. Wijaya E., M. C. Frith, P. Horton, and K. Asai. 2013. Finding protein-coding genes through human polymorphisms. *PLoS ONE*. 8 (1): e54210.

7. Demuth, J. P. et al. 2006. The evolution of mammalian gene families. *PLoS ONE*. 1 (1): e85.

8. Clamp, M. et al. 2007. Distinguishing protein-coding and noncoding genes in the human genome. *Proceedings of the National Academy of Sciences*. 104 (49): 19428-33.

9. Wu, D. D., D. M. Irwin, and Y. P. Zhang. 2011. De novo origin of human protein-coding genes. *PLoS Genetics*. 7 (11): e1002379.

10. Ruiz-Orera, J. et al. 2015. Origins of De Novo Genes in Human and Chimpanzee. *PLoS Genetics*. 11 (12): e1005721.

11. Colbourne, J. K. et al. 2011. The ecoresponsive genome of *Daphnia pulex*. *Science*. 331 (6017): 555-561.

12. Zhang, G. et al. 2012. The oyster genome reveals stress adaptation and complexity of shell formation. *Nature*. 490 (7418): 49-54.

13. Yang, L. et al., 2013. Genome-wide identification, characterization, and expression analysis of lineage-specific genes within zebrafish. *BMC Genomics*. 14 (65): 1471-2164.

7 Evolutionary Pseudogenes—Not Pseudo Anymore

Summary: Pseudogenes are claimed to be genetic fossils of broken genes littering our genome as useless relics. Evolutionists speculate that pseudogenes somehow became broken over time and currently serve no purpose. But as research progresses, these genes have been shown to be active and functional key regulators of human health. These findings clearly point to design throughout the human genome.

What Are Pseudogenes?

One of the popular past arguments for evidence of DNA sequence evolution in the human genome has been the speculation that it contains inherited gene-based "shared mistakes" with chimps called pseudogenes. These once enigmatic DNA sequences were originally thought to be the defunct remnants of genes. In other words, they were thought to represent nothing more than genomic fossils littering our genome as useless relics of evolution. Of course, like other evolutionary speculations of misunderstood DNA sequence, the whole pseudogene paradigm is being completely up-ended by new discoveries.

Pseudogenes come in several variants based on the presence or absence of certain DNA sequence features.[1] One category is termed the unprocessed pseudogene that contains all the normal parts of a typical protein-coding gene but is thought to be inactivated based on presumed DNA code errors that disrupt their eventual translation into a functional protein. While many of these unprocessed pseudogenes have no observed protein product, they do produce functional RNA molecules that are key components regulating the function and activity of other genes and gene networks. As is the case with most genes, evolutionists speculate that unprocessed pseudogenes arose as the result of being duplicated from another gene. Once again, for most of these that have been studied this is nothing but mere speculation.

The Beta-Globin Pseudogene—A Case Study in Evolutionary Failure

The beta-globin pseudogene has been one of the leading arguments used to promote human evolution and the myth of shared genetic mistakes with chimpanzees.[2] The beta-globin pseudogene is considered to be of the unprocessed type of pseudogene and, thanks to the fact that the gene neighborhood in which it is located called the beta-globin locus, is a heavily studied region for gene regulation in humans. Because of biomedical research in this area of the genome, we are beginning to better understand the importance of pseudogenes and how they work and function as critical key gene regulators.

Hemoglobin is a required protein in human red blood cells that binds to and transports oxygen throughout the body's circulatory system. The human hemoglobin

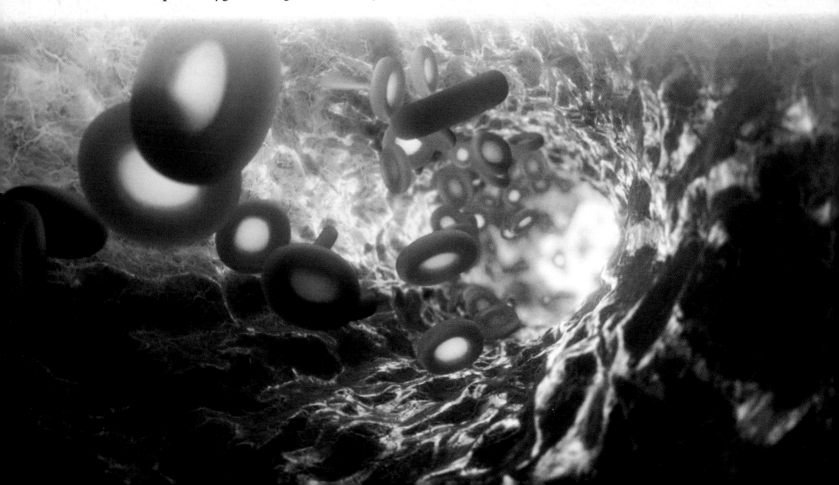

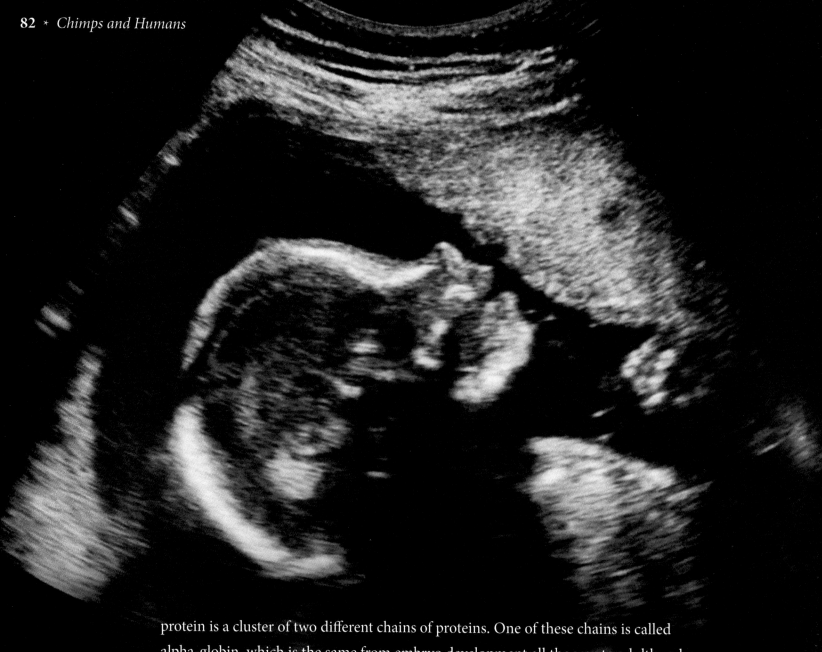

protein is a cluster of two different chains of proteins. One of these chains is called alpha-globin, which is the same from embryo development all the way to adulthood. The second protein component is called the beta-hemoglobin chain that specifically changes at the embryo-to-fetal transition and again at the fetal-to-adult transition. This amazing engineering allows the developing embryo, fetus, and then newborn baby to receive oxygen at precisely correct levels throughout its critical growth processes and developmental transitions.

The beta-globin proteins that are switched out during this amazing process are encoded in a cluster of six genes that contains over 80,000 bases on human chromosome 11. The growth-stage-specific expression of each gene in the cluster is dependent on that specific gene's interactive regulation by a genetic control region preceding the whole gene cluster called the locus control region, or LCR.

While five out of the six genes in the beta-globin cluster produce functional proteins, one of the genes given the name *HBBP1*, otherwise called the beta-globin pseudogene, produces a long noncoding regulatory RNA.[2] The lack of a protein product produced by the *HBBP1* gene was originally predicted based on a number of stop signals found in its DNA code that were errantly predicted to be mutations. As a result of this hasty judgement, the *HBBP1* gene was originally classified as a broken defunct DNA fossil remnant because of its assumed nonfunctionality. And because a similar version of the *HBBP1* gene, along with its presumed DNA sequence errors, is also found in chimpanzees, evolutionists claimed it as proof that humans inherited their broken version from a common ancestor shared with chimps. This whole idea is essentially the basis of the inherited mistakes paradigm, and the *HBBP1* gene was routinely held up as the poster child example.

Interestingly, one of the main problems with the whole shared mistakes idea is the actual evidence for the claim. Molecular evolutionists who study DNA sequence and make predictions from it have been curious as to why, if the *HBBP1* gene is nonfunctional, its sequence has not mutated significantly over the past three to six million years of alleged human evolution.[2-3] In the evolutionary mindset, nonfunctional DNA has no selective restraints on it as does functional sequence, which they believe mutates much less. In other words, the purported evidence for common ancestry in this sequence actually argues against it being nonfunctional. Whether you are a creationist or an evolutionist, a highly conserved gene that is very similar across taxa typically indicates that it is serving a common functional purpose in both humans and chimps.

Quite interestingly, a fairly recent research paper was published in the journal *Genome Biology and Evolution* that now confirms the fact that the *HBBP1* gene is highly resistant to mutation and is in fact functional.[3] In this study, scientists compared the beta-globin gene clusters in many different individuals among humans the world over and also within populations of chimpanzees. Quite shockingly, of the six genes in the entire beta-globin cluster, the *HBBP1* gene and its companion, the *HBD* gene that it's connected to, are highly nonvariable compared to the other beta-globin genes. These results indicate that very little mutation is tolerated in the *HBBP1* gene, vindicating that it is functionally important.

But the data get even more exciting. The researchers then analyzed the *HBBP1* so-called pseudogene gene-function data and found that it's actively associated with gene regulation in conjunction with the LCR region mentioned above that literally controls the whole beta-globin gene cluster. In yet another research publication, the researchers produced data that clearly show that the regulatory activity of the *HBBP1* pseudogene is connected to a wide variety of functional sites over the entire beta-globin cluster. Interestingly, the *HBBP1* was actually a busy little bee with 74 different network site connections in the human genome associated with gene regulation.[4]

In fact, my own research has shown that in one database, the *HBBP1* had gene expression activity in brain, endothelial, epithelial, fibroblast, hematopoietic, liver, muscle, and stem cells.[2] Another database called BioGPS listed significant levels of gene expression for the *HBBP1* gene in 84 different specific tissue and cell types. This translates into the *HBBP1* gene being expressed in 28 out of 31 major categorical tissue groupings in the human body.

All of this new functional data combined with the fact that *HBBP1* tolerates very little mutation meshes well with another recent study showing that a single-base mutation in the *HBBP1* pseudogene is associated with a blood disease called beta-thalasemia.[5]

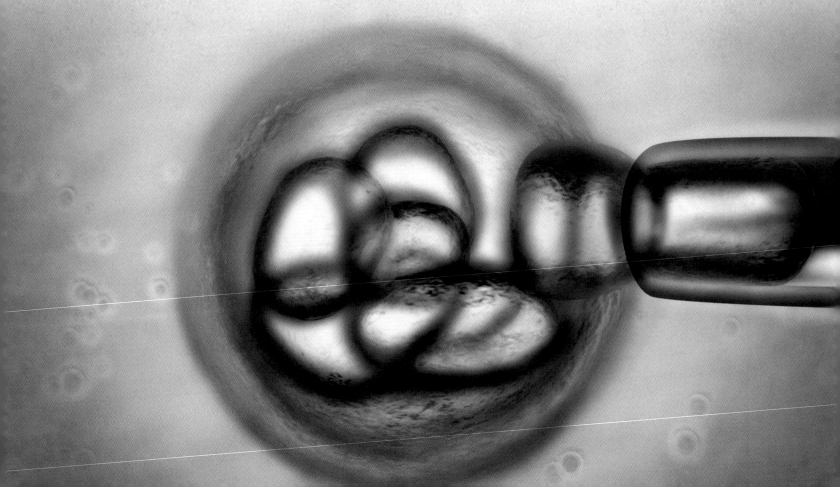

Instead of being a useless mutated remnant according to failed evolutionary predictions, the *HBBP1* beta-globin pseudogene is clearly genetically active and plays a key functional role as a cleverly engineered feature programmed by God the Creator.

Retrogenes Are Functional Too

Another type of alleged fossil gene is called a processed pseudogene because it typically lacks intervening noncoding sequences called introns. Most genes in plants and animals have both coding (called exons) and noncoding segments (called introns) and are in pieces, so to speak. After an RNA is copied from the gene, the noncoding introns are spliced out by cell machinery. Because processed pseudogenes lack introns, evolutionists have speculated that they arose from the sequence of a gene's RNA (called a messenger RNA, or mRNA) that was then reinserted into the genome as a genetic accident. Another commonly used name for these types of pseudogenes is retrogenes.

Despite the still-prevalent paradigm that processed pseudogenes are also thought to be genomic fossils, scientists have been identifying important functions for retrogenes in mammals for over 30 years.[6-7] In 2013, I described the discovery of a life-critical function for the human retrogene called *PPM1K*.[8] Scientists first realized that the *PPM1K* pseudogene was being actively transcribed (producing long noncoding RNAs), and when the cells of cancer patients were examined, the *PPM1K* RNAs were found in abnormally low levels compared to the cells of healthy humans.[9] The *PPM1K* RNAs were not only shown to help regulate the protein-coding counterpart of the *PPM1K* gene, from which it allegedly evolved, but also another gene called *NEK8* that has also been implicated with cancerous cell growth. The bottom line is that if this pseudogene is not functioning properly, cellular dysfunction and cancer are the most likely result.

The *GULO* Pseudogene: Broken but Not Shared

In some cases, there are genes in the genome that are actually damaged and broken due to the fact that the human genome is devolving or degrading over time, not evolving and improving. Because of ingenious built-in systems of resilience engineered into our DNA and bodies, we can still survive. In fact, the burden of mutations in the DNA are increasing in humans as I discuss in another chapter in a process that Cornell University geneticist John Sanford has called genetic entropy. In the case of one particular broken gene, the *GULO* pseudogene, evolutionists have tried to use it as an example of shared mistakes with apes. But a more detailed analysis of the actual genomic data indicates otherwise.

In the case of the *GULO* gene, geneticists have found that it's actually broken in a wide variety of animals, including humans, apes, some birds, some bats, Guinea pigs, some mice, and some pigs.[10] In the cases of birds and bats, the broken nature of the gene doesn't follow any sort of evolutionary pattern.[10] In other words, some types of birds and bats that have functional *GULO* genes, according to evolution, somehow magically descended from other types with broken *GULO* genes. The problem is how these genes could have fixed themselves if that was actually the case. As a creationist and believing that God created different bird kinds and different bat kinds, this lineage-specific type of mutational event is easily explained under a model of Genesis kinds and genetic entropy. After extensively studying the *GULO* gene across the spectrum of life, it became obvious to me that it was susceptible to being broken in a fallen world, and that organisms could make up for the loss of its function by taking in vitamin C from the foods they ate.

As it pertains to the idea that humans inherited a broken version of the *GULO* gene from an ape ancestor, it turns out that the entire argument is cherry-picked and based on only a very small fragment of the gene that is similar between humans and apes. When the entire gene region is compared between humans, chimps, gorillas, and orangutans, it becomes obvious that we are seeing the same lineage-specific pattern of deletions and breaks that are found in bats and birds. No pattern of evolution whatsoever is apparent.[10] In fact, what tipped me off to this fact was a research paper that I read published by evolutionists in which they admitted that when the entire gene was used to perform evolutionary analyses, they could not generate phylogenetic trees that matched with evolutionary predictions.[11]

When I found out that the *GULO* gene sequence as a whole was not supportive of the human-ape evolutionary paradigm, I decided to do an in-depth analysis of my own. Sure enough, the *GULO* gene had been broken in different ways that gave different patterns in humans, chimps, gorillas, and orangutans. From the data, it became clear that the breaks had occurred around different classes of repetitive DNA sequences that tend to be more susceptible to mutation and degeneration than other areas. However, even when I performed evolutionary tree analyses with the protein-coding segments that were still intact, I could not get phylogenetic trees that matched the evolutionary paradigm for five out of the six exons. Of course, the whole focus of the cherry-picking done by evolutionists was on exon number 5 that gave them the results that they wanted. The reality of the *GULO* gene data is that it proves not only that humans are unique, but that chimps, gorillas, and orangutans are each unique created ape kinds.

Egg-Laying Pseudogenes That Don't Exist

The BioLogos organization is an evangelical group that promotes hypothetical macroevolutionary speculation as if it were real applied science. One of the leading arguments they put forth in their human evolutionary propaganda is the idea that the human genome contains the remnant of an egg-laying gene we supposedly inherited from birds in our distant past. As the story goes, it's proposed that an egg-yolk related vitellogenin (vtg) gene was acquired through descent from a common ancestor shared with chickens and that the remnants of this gene can be found in our DNA. Oddly, BioLogos is the only evolutionary organization that uses this angle as a major argument in their human evolution propaganda.

Since previous stories of inherited pseudogenes from alleged evolutionary ancestors I had investigated proved to contain data that contradicted and debunked their evolutionary claims, I decided to investigate this speculative tale as well.[12] The whole basis of this so-called fossil in our DNA is based on a meager 150 bases that are only 62% identical to its comparable counterpart in exon 3 of the chicken vtg1 gene. This is a tiny representative portion of the actual chicken vtg1 gene, which is 42,637 bases long, not including its preceding regulatory promoter sequence. So, the alleged vtg gene fragment in human DNA actually represents less than 1% of its supposed original ancestral gene. Even in a theoretical evolutionary sense, to claim that a pseudogene can be identified by only 0.35% of its original sequence is quite a stretch of the Darwinian imagination.

However, when I really dove into the data, I found out that the real story is that the alleged 150-base vtg sequence is not a pseudogene remnant at all but a functional genetic switch called an enhancer element that is located in the fifth intron of a genomic address messenger (GAM) gene. This particular GAM gene has biomedical importance because it produces long noncoding RNAs that have been experimentally shown to selectively inhibit the translation (protein production) of specific target genes that have been implicated in a number of human diseases. Messenger RNAs from this GAM gene are also proven to be active in a variety of human brain tissues in both fetal and adult subjects.

Once again, when the actual genetic data are more fully investigated, an anti-evolutionary story emerges. The data clearly show that the alleged vtg pseudogene fragment is a functional enhancer element in a GAM gene that is active in the human brain, which overturns the idea that the sequence is an egg-laying gene fossil.

Human Pseudogene Summary

One of the most popular arguments for alleged evidence of human-ape evolution in the genome has been the paradigm of pseudogenes. These once-enigmatic DNA sequences were speculated to be the defunct broken remnants of genes, thought to represent nothing but genomic fossils. However, huge amounts of new research publicly available in a variety of databases and also described in research publications are proving that many pseudogenes are functional and key genetic regulators of human health. So why do these presumptuous evolutionary predictions about the human genome continually falter in light of new advances in genetics research? These repeated failures are due to the fact that scientists who possess an evolutionary mindset are errantly

❝Considerably more progress would be made in biomedical genetics if scientists approached the genome from the perspective of pervasive functionality and purposeful bioengineering as the handiwork of an omnipotent and all-wise Creator.❞

perceiving the genome as the product of chance random processes, not purposeful design. Instead, considerably more progress would be made in biomedical genetics if scientists approached the genome from the perspective of pervasive functionality and purposeful bioengineering as the handiwork of an omnipotent and all-wise Creator.

References

1. Tomkins, J. P. 2013. Pseudogenes Are Functional, Not Genomic Fossils. *Acts & Facts.* 42 (7): 9.
2. Tomkins, J. P. 2013. The Human Beta-Globin Pseudogene Is Non-variable and Functional. *Answers Research Journal.* 6: 293-302.
3. Moleirinho, A. et al. 2013. Evolutionary Constraints in the β-Globin Cluster: The Signature of Purifying Selection at the δ-Globin (HBD) Locus and its Role in Developmental Gene Regulation. *Genome Biology and Evolution.* 5 (3): 559–571.
4. Sheffield, N. C. et al. 2013. Patterns of regulatory activity across diverse human cell types predict tissue identity, transcription factor binding, and long-range interactions. *Genome Research.* 23 (5): 777-788.
5. Giannopoulou, E. et al. 2012. A Single Nucleotide Polymorphism in the HBBP1 Gene in the Human β-Globin Locus is Associated with a Mild β-Thalassemia Disease Phenotype. *Hemoglobin.* 36 (5): 433-445.
6. Soares, M. B. et al. 1985. RNA-mediated gene duplication: the rat preproinsulin I gene is a functional retroposon. *Molecular and Cellular Biology.* 5 (8): 2090-2103.
7. Ciomborowska, J. et al. 2013. "Orphan" Retrogenes in the Human Genome. *Molecular Biology Evolution.* 30 (2): 384–396.
8. Tomkins, J. P. Pseudogene Plays Important Role in Cell Cycle. *Creation Science Update.* Posted on ICR.org April 12, 2013, accessed January 30, 2019.
9. Chan, W. L. et al. 2013. Transcribed pseudogene ψPPM1K generates endogenous siRNA to suppress oncogenic cell growth in hepatocellular carcinoma. *Nucleic Acids Research.* 41 (6): 3734-3747.
10. Tomkins, J. P. 2014. The Human GULO Pseudogene - Evidence for Evolutionary Discontinuity and Genetic Entropy. *Answers Research Journal.* 7: 91-101.
11. Lachapelle, M. Y. and G. Drouin. 2011. Inactivation dates of the human and guinea pig vitamin C genes. *Genetica.* 139 (2): 199-207.
12. Tomkins, J. P. 2015. Challenging the BioLogos Claim that a Vitellogenin (Egg-Laying) Pseudogene Exists in the Human Genome. *Answers Research Journal.* 8: 403-411.

8 Incomplete Lineage Sorting

Summary: Evolutionists have long attempted to develop a genetic lineage between chimp and human that points to a common ancestor. But as more human and ape DNA sequence data are analyzed, these supposed relationships are increasingly unclear, incomplete, and unpredicted. No clear evolutionary tree emerges. Rather, we see individual species within kinds each with their own genealogy—just like we'd expect if each kind were uniquely created.

Incomplete lineage sorting (ILS) is one of those never-ending confounding problems in the field of evolutionary biology that has plagued the fictional dogma of common descent on a grand neo-Darwinian scale for many years. Amazingly, this evolution-negating enigma has also been fairly well suppressed from most of the general public and scientific circles outside the field of molecular phylogenetics.

ILS Among Humans and Apes

Since the days of Darwin, evolutionists have promoted the idea that humans and the great apes are recent branches on the grand evolutionary tree that lead back to a common ape ancestor. A single branch on this evolutionary or phylogenetic tree is typically referred to as a lineage. For example, there is the human lineage, the chimp lineage, the gorilla lineage, and the orangutan lineage (Figure 1). Evolutionists claim that humans are closest to the chimp lineage and actually share a mythical common ancestor.

The ILS evolutionary conundrum as illustrated among humans and the great apes is characterized by the well-established fact that large numbers of DNA segments show no clear pattern of common ancestry when using them to construct evolutionary trees. Depending on the pieces of DNA being compared, some segments of human DNA are more related to gorilla than to chimp, and vice versa. The same unruly evolutionary tree patterns are found when orangutan DNA is thrown into the mix.

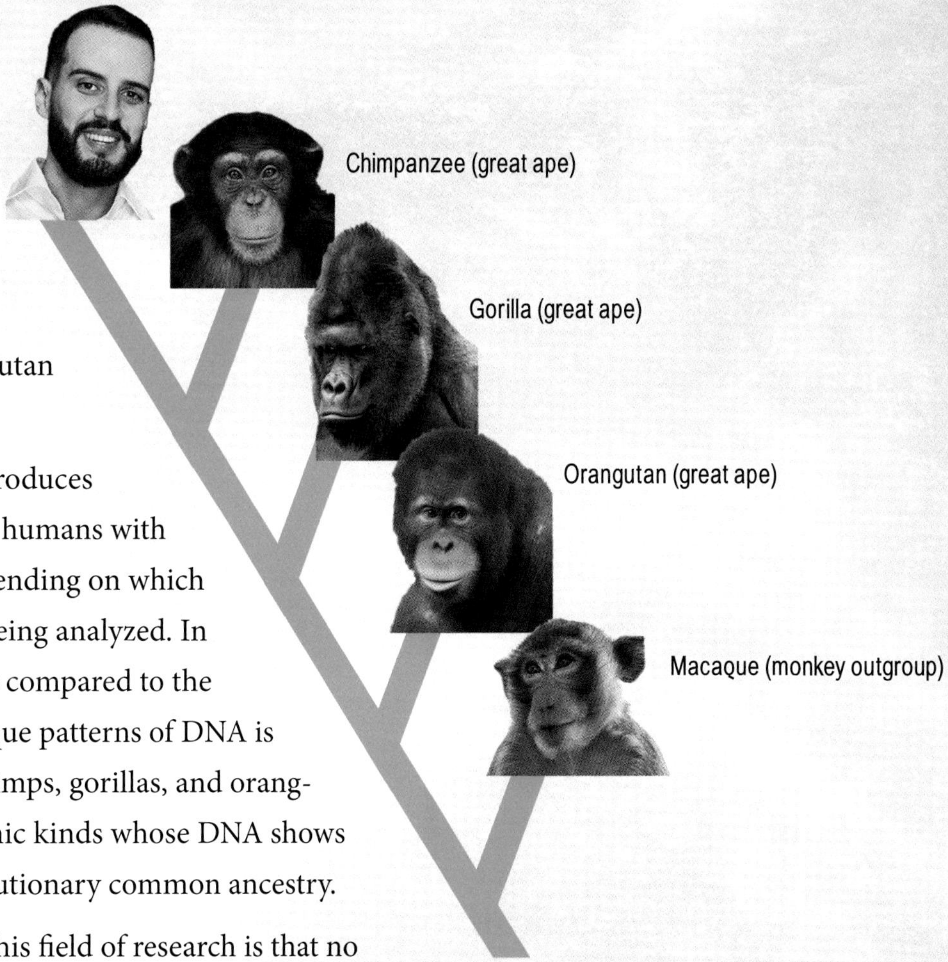

Figure 1. Standard evolutionary tree (phylogeny) for human evolution

This well-established fact produces different evolutionary trees for humans with the different types of apes, depending on which group of DNA sequences are being analyzed. In other words, when humans are compared to the different apes, a mosaic of unique patterns of DNA is produced. Clearly, humans, chimps, gorillas, and orangutans are each unique taxonomic kinds whose DNA shows no clear overall pattern of evolutionary common ancestry.

The little-known secret of this field of research is that no coherent model of primate evolution can be achieved by theoretical evolutionary biologists. And as the amount of DNA sequence in the public databases keeps growing, the inconvenient problem of ILS keeps getting worse for the human evolution paradigm.

Human and Chimp DNA Lack Common Ancestry

Shortly after the first chimp genome paper was published, discussed in chapter 2, the first study showing that large levels of ILS existed between humans and chimps was published by a secular evolutionary group.[1] Making the results of this study even more spectacular was the fact that the researchers filtered and manipulated the data as much as possible to improve the possibility of an evolutionarily favorable outcome.

Despite the efforts at data manipulation, the outcome showed that no clear path of common ancestry existed between humans and any great ape. The researchers started with a large pool of human, chimp, gorilla, orangutan, and rhesus macaque (a monkey outgroup) DNA sequences that were found to be common to all taxon. The goal was to use these various common sequences in a DNA comparison technique called a multiple alignment. The end result is a data set that can be used to construct evolutionary tree diagrams.

The original set of DNA sequences were put through several levels of selection to pre-analyze, trim, and filter them to make the multiple sequence alignments work optimally. A starting set of about 30,000 sequences were chosen that shared DNA between humans and the four ape/monkey species. These were then aligned in the initial stage, and only those that produced at least 300 DNA letter matches were kept for a second series of alignments. From the second level of alignments, only those that yielded superior statistical probabilities for high levels of sequence matching were used in the final analysis.

Despite all the levels of data filtering to produce the most favorable DNA sequence matches and evolutionary trees, the results produced high levels of what evolutionists call discordant data—meaning the data contradicted evolution. Most importantly, the results did not show any clear overall path of common ancestry between humans and apes. What emerged from the study was a mosaic of human and ape DNA sequence similarity trajectories that presented no consensus evolutionary pattern of common ancestry. In fact, the best summary of the results can be found in the researcher's own words:

Rhesus monkeys

Thus, in two-thirds of the cases a genealogy results in which humans and chimpanzees are not each other's closest genetic relatives. The corresponding genealogies are incongruent with the species tree. In accordance with the experimental evidences, this implies that there is no such thing as a unique evolutionary history of the human genome. Rather, it resembles a patchwork of individual regions following their own genealogy.[1]

> "For about 23% of our genome, we share no immediate genetic ancestry with our closest living relative, the chimpanzee."

The authors also add that the lack of support for a consistent evolutionary relationship among humans and apes is due to the "inclusion of alignments with no clear phylogenetic [evolutionary] signal."[1] This a rather profound statement by the researchers in light of the fact that they employed large amounts of data filtering and DNA sequence selection with the sole purpose of providing enormous levels of "phylogenetic signals." In other words, the data were heavily manipulated to be as favorable to evolution as possible. What more could the researchers have possibly asked for? Despite the efforts in this study to steer the data toward an evolutionary outcome, the truth that humans did not evolve from a common ancestor with chimps triumphed over the failed dogma of evolution.

The Gorilla Genome—Bad ILS News for Evolution

In the overall model of human-ape evolution, it's believed that the next-closest ancestor to humans besides chimp is the gorilla. In 2012, the first major draft and analysis of the gorilla genome was completed. Once again, the data did not fit the evolutionary paradigm. According to the researchers of this study, "in 30% of the genome, gorilla is closer to human or chimpanzee than the latter are to each other."[2] The results of this research confirmed the same patterns of ILS that had shown up in the previous study discussed above.

Another very interesting result from this study was that human, chimp, and gorilla were each found to have at least 500 of their own unique protein-coding genes specific to their taxon. We touched on this idea of organism-specific genes to some extent in the chapter on orphan genes (taxonomically restricted genes). So, not only were there large groups of genes unique to humans but also within the taxons of chimps and gorillas. In other words, chimps appear to be uniquely different from gorillas as much as they are to humans and vice versa.

In regard to the overall evolution-negating patterns of ILS observed in the gorilla genome study, the authors stated:

> Across the genome we find 30% of bases exhibiting ILS, with no significant difference between the number sorting as ((H,G),C) and ((C,G),H). However, the fraction of ILS varies with respect to genomic position by more than expected under a model of genome-wide neutral evolution.[2]

In other words, 30% of the DNA segments studied showed no clear pattern of evolutionary common descent between humans, gorillas, and chimps. In addition, these evolutionary anomalies showed no clear ancestral patterns related to their positions in the genome. Given the standard common ancestry proposed for man's evolution from an ape, the genetic data do not fit the model.

ILS of Nonvariable DNA Debunks Evolution

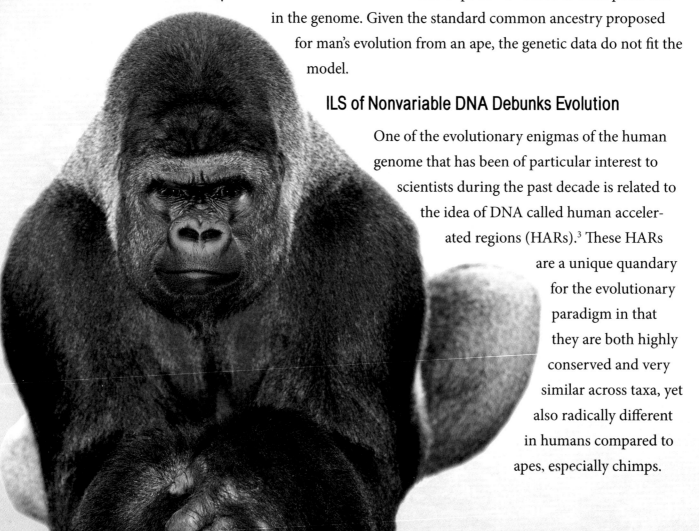

One of the evolutionary enigmas of the human genome that has been of particular interest to scientists during the past decade is related to the idea of DNA called human accelerated regions (HARs).[3] These HARs are a unique quandary for the evolutionary paradigm in that they are both highly conserved and very similar across taxa, yet also radically different in humans compared to apes, especially chimps.

Scientists speculate that these genetic differences arose from rapid evolution in these particular areas since the time that humans allegedly diverged from apes.

The presence of HARs is highly problematic for evolutionists because they tend to be highly conserved or similar in sequence identity across vertebrates yet are markedly different in humans.[3] In the evolutionary mindset, DNA sequences that stay the same across taxon are restrained from evolving. Yet another problem with HARs is that within supposed vertebrate evolutionary lineages many are taxonomically isolated and seem to arise suddenly with no prior evolutionary history.

I researched and published a phylogenetic analysis of 105 HAR genes in 10 different vertebrate taxa and showed that these sequences display remarkable evolutionary discordance on a broad scale.[3] Just like the other ILS studies done by secular scientists, these results clearly show that humans and each ape taxon are uniquely created with no clear pattern of evolutionary ancestry. The data are more consistent with the creation model, wherein the genes that encode taxonomic distinction were custom-designed for that taxon.

One HAR sequence of particular note is called HAR1, which was the first popularized discovery of a 118-base region that had 18 different bases out of 118 (85% similarity) compared to its counterpart in the chimpanzee genome.[4] When this particular HAR gene was analyzed for its variability among humans, it was found to be completely nonvariable and identical across human populations. Making this discovery even more remarkable was that when the same DNA segment from chimpanzee and chicken were compared, there was only a two-base difference out of the 118 bases, making chimp and chicken 98% similar for this particular DNA segment. If evolution made sense, then why was this region highly conserved across taxa but so different between humans and chimps?

Evolutionists Explain ILS with More Circular Reasoning

Of course, ILS based on DNA sequence and the problems it presents for the evolutionary paradigm of common ancestry are nothing new. The ILS problem actually existed before the days of DNA sequencing in regard to mosaics of morphological traits. For example, gorillas have ears and hands that are more similar to humans than they are to chimps, yet humans are thought to be more closely related to chimps. Even orangutans have morphological features that are more similar to humans than either chimps or gorillas. In fact, a paper was published in 2009 describing how orangutans should be humans' closest ancestor based on morphological features.[5]

So how does the evolutionist grapple with ILS and its confounding issues? If you read the earlier chapter about orphan genes, it was shown that evolutionists call upon circular reasoning to obfuscate the issue without really solving it. Evolutionary explanations for ILS basically involve the same type of circular reasoning. The evolutionist explains ILS by claiming that it's caused by incongruence in lineages and that incongruent lineages are caused by ILS. Both terms are essentially describing the same thing or problem with neither actually providing a solution to the dilemma.

Another so-called explanation for ILS is that it came about by segments of DNA being randomly exchanged across populations. However, this idea is completely irrelevant when applied to organisms that are completely unrelated taxon and not interfertile. If there is no reproductive way to exchange DNA, then the random distribution of DNA across or within populations is a nonissue. In other words, they can't mate and exchange DNA to make ILS happen.

In the standard evolutionary paradigm, it's speculated that humans diverged from a common ape-like ancestor with chimps and thus lost their inter-fertility or capacity to exchange DNA about three to six million years ago. The alleged presence of ILS in humans and apes has no plausible naturalistic explanation because humans, chimps, gorillas, and orangutans are not freely exchanging DNA amongst themselves. And if you ascribe to the evolutionary story, they have not done so for over three million years or more.

The clear fact of the matter is that the whole ILS data quagmire is bad news for evolution and always has been. In a published review on the increasing presence of ILS in the massive amounts of DNA sequence data that is causing evolutionary theory so much grief, researchers stated, "Indeed, several recent studies have reported on massive amounts of incongruence in various data sets due to incomplete lineage sorting."[6]

Besides invoking circular reasoning and improbable ideas about gene flow to explain the ILS anomaly, evolutionists also use a variety of methodologies that average and smooth out all of the inconsistencies, combined with a healthy dose of data filtering and manipulation. Obviously, this data should not simply be "averaged out", it should be accepted for the true discontinuity and creature-kind specificity that it truly represents.

Conclusion: ILS Proves Human Uniqueness, Not Evolution

Incomplete lineage sorting (ILS) is a well-documented consequence produced when constructing phylogenetic (evolutionary) trees using DNA sequence data for humans and apes (e.g., chimpanzee, orangutan, gorilla). In fact, in a 2013 journal paper, I documented how ILS debunks evolution and proves the Genesis creation account across the entire spectrum of life in a thorough review of the scientific literature related to secular research in the so-called evolutionary tree of life.[7] The clear fact of ILS demonstrates that evolutionary trees derived from DNA sequence are routinely inconsistent and incongruent. They are different from the predicted hypothetical path of evolutionary common descent.

> **"The overall consensus outcome is that no clear path of common ancestry between humans and apes exists such that no coherent model of human evolution can be achieved."**

The ILS enigma for evolution is characterized by segments of DNA sequence that are either protein-coding or noncoding that yield completely different lineages or paths of evolutionary descent when constructing evolutionary trees depending on the DNA sequence being used for the analysis. With the recent massive increase of different ape genome sequences in the public databases, the quest to produce a coherent evolutionary lineage of descent between humans and apes is even more thoroughly confounded. The overall consensus outcome is that no clear path of common ancestry between humans and apes exists such that no coherent model of human evolution can be achieved.

References

1. Ebersberger, I. et al. 2007. Mapping human genetic ancestry. *Molecular Biology and Evolution*. 24 (10): 2266-2276.
2. Scally, A. et al. 2012. Insights into hominid evolution from the gorilla genome sequence. *Nature*. 483 (7388): 169-175.
3. Tomkins, J. P. 2016. Human Uniqueness and Accelerated Storytelling: How Conserved Regulatory Regions in the Genome Challenge Evolution. *Creation Research Society Quarterly*. 52: 256-264.
4. Pollard, K. S. et al. 2006. Forces shaping the fastest evolving regions in the human genome. *PLoS Genetics*. 2 (10): e168.
5. Grehan, J. R. and J. H. Schwartz. 2009. Evolution of the second orangutan: phylogeny and biogeography of hominid origins. *Journal of Biogeography*. 36 (10): 1823-1844.
6. Yu, Y. et al. 2011. Coalescent Histories on Phylogenetic Networks and Detection of Hybridization Despite Incomplete Lineage Sorting. *Systematic Biology*. 60 (2): 138-149.
7. Tomkins, J. and J. Bergman. 2013. Incomplete lineage sorting and other 'rogue' data fell the tree of life. *Journal of Creation*. 27: 84-92.

9 Gene Function Differences

Summary: Studies show that gene expression in humans is significantly different from the expression found in chimpanzees, especially in the brain, where one study showed that 90% of the human genes were turned on at significantly higher levels than chimpanzee genes. Another study showed the brain DNA sequences of both species didn't match evolutionary descent predictions for a common ancestor.

Functional Genomics—A New Frontier

In addition to the major differences that exist between the human and chimp genomes in regard to DNA similarity, chromosome numbers, Y chromosome DNA, orphan genes, and incomplete lineage sorting, there are also major differences in how genes are utilized or turned on or expressed. Humans and chimps, like other mammals, have fairly similar cell biochemistries and general gross morphological similarities as well. Therefore, we actually share some high levels of similarity in DNA sequence that is performing the same basic cellular function.

New genomic technologies allow scientists to compare thousands of genes from different types of organisms to see if they are turned off and on similarly, how much of the gene product is produced, and what other genes they interact with in the form of

> "These large gene function differences clearly show the large chasm that exists in the genetics between humans and apes."

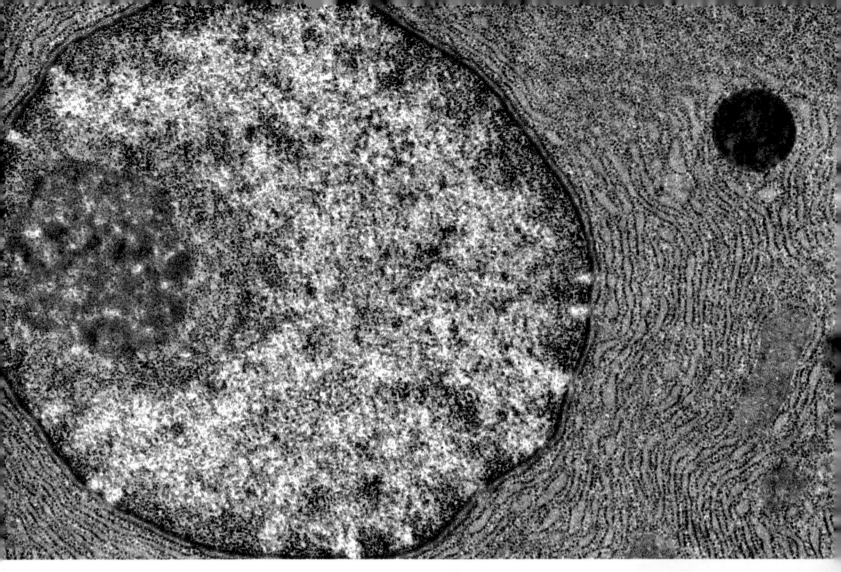

False-color transmission electron microscopy shows the nucleus of a protein-synthesizing cell. The nuclear envelope (red), chromatin (green), and nucleolus (blue) can be seen.

networks. Of course, these data are dependent on the type of tissue (organ), age of the tissue, and various other factors influencing the organism and its tissues.

In these types of studies, scientists are discovering many significant differences in gene expression between humans and chimps. These large gene function differences clearly show the large chasm that exists in the genetics between humans and apes.

Protein Similarities and Differences

The functional outcome of what is traditionally referred to as a gene is a protein that's a specifically three-dimensional folded chain of ordered amino acids encoded for by the DNA sequence in the gene. After an RNA copy of a gene is made, the messenger RNA is taken out of the nucleus into the cytoplasm, and a protein is produced according to its sequence. Proteins can also be combined with other proteins, sugars, metal ions, and RNAs to form larger functional complexes.

It's estimated that less than 5% of the human genome actually contains sequence that directly specifies the amino acid sequence in proteins. In their efforts to find DNA that is similar between humans and chimps, evolutionists have primarily focused on comparing just the protein-coding sequences that are similar between humans and chimps. However, even this strategy has turned up surprising results in regard to how these genes differ in their function between humans and chimps.

Gene Expression Differences

Genes are encoded in pieces by the Creator to increase their utility and functionality. The segments that code for protein are called exons, while the intervening regions are called introns. Before being used to make a protein, the messenger RNA copied from a gene is processed by complex cellular machinery that involves the splicing out of the introns in the RNA and the joining together of the exons. During this process, exons can be omitted, doubled, or even added in from another gene. As a result, a single gene can produce many different variants like a Swiss army knife. This whole process is called alternative splicing and is tightly regulated according to the specific needs of the cell.

Alternative splicing for a single gene can generate many protein variants depending on the gene. See Figure 1 for a graphic illustration of alternative splicing. These splice variations fall under very complex regulatory genetic control mechanisms. In fact, the first such research in 2007 showed that alternative splicing differs significantly between humans and chimps. The authors of the paper state, "Surprisingly, 6%–8% of profiled orthologous [similar] exons display pronounced splicing level differences in the corresponding tissues from the two species." In such cases of distinct differences, the typical explanation is always rapid evolution. The researchers go on to say, "These layers of regulation have evolved rapidly."[1]

In a 2018 paper using even more advanced technology and also throwing Rhesus macaque in the mix, the researchers found that "in total, 1526 exons and exon sets from 1236 genes showed significant splicing differences among primates."[2] The uniqueness of human was especially profound in that "the increase in isoform inclusion levels [gene variants], showed a 2-fold acceleration on the human evolutionary lineage when compared with the chimpanzee lineage."[2] Once again, such so-called rapid "2-fold" evolution expressed in human uniqueness of alternative splicing for

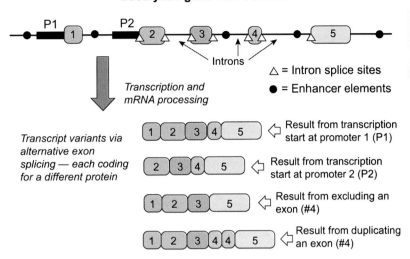

Eucaryotic gene with 5 exons

△ = Intron splice sites
● = Enhancer elements

Transcription and mRNA processing

Transcript variants via alternative exon splicing — each coding for a different protein

Result from transcription start at promoter 1 (P1)

Result from transcription start at promoter 2 (P2)

Result from excluding an exon (#4)

Result from duplicating an exon (#4)

Figure 1. Diagram of a hypothetical eukaryotic gene with five exons (protein-coding regions). As illustrated, the highly controlled process of alternative splicing allows for the creation of multiple proteins being produced from a single gene via the creative usage and placement of exons.

genes previously determined to be highly evolutionarily similar does not support the Darwinian paradigm.

While a number of common mammalian protein-coding genes share similarity between humans and chimps, the features regulating these genes appear to play a huge role in the observed differences between apes and humans.[3] As early as 1975, before the days of modern genomics, scientists speculated that the many obvious differences between human and apes were due to factors controlling the expression of genes.[4]

Determining differences in gene expression across the whole genome is a complicated question to both investigate and answer. In humans and chimps, we would expect minor regulatory differences between highly similar genes that perform common biochemical functions in mammals as a general rule. Therefore, scientists have focused on areas that make humans unique, such as brain function. In fact, these types of investigations are where many profound genetic differences between humans and chimps have been discovered.

One of the first studies undertaken along this line of reasoning was in 2003, in which 169 different brain genes were found to be expressed in a markedly different manner in human, chimp, and macaque cerebral cortexes.[5] Of these genes, 90% were

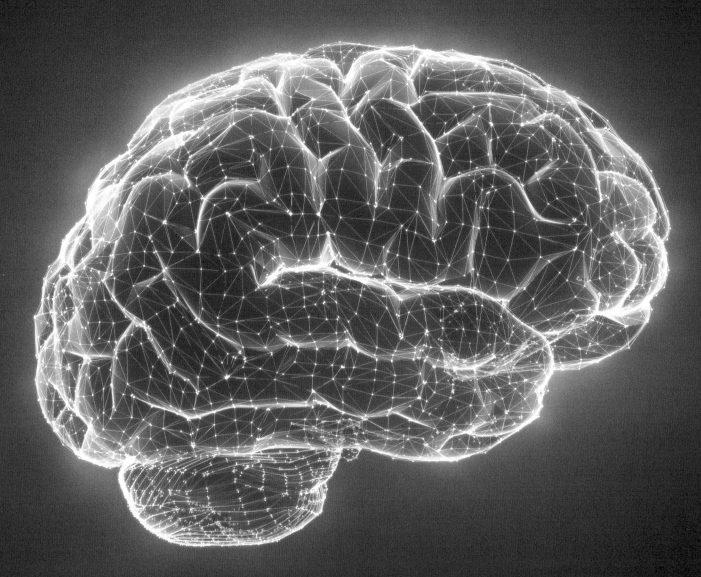

turned on at significantly higher levels in humans compared to chimp. The researchers reported, "The human brain displays a distinctive pattern of gene expression relative to non-human primates, with higher expression levels for many genes belonging to a wide variety of functional classes."[5]

Expression Patterns Contradict Evolution

A later study in 2010 confirmed and expanded upon these striking observations and revealed that 1,872 genes in the frontal cortex of the human brain exhibited marked expression differences compared to chimp.[6] Increasing the anti-evolutionary mystery of these findings was the fact that the authors also discovered that when the DNA sequences of these genes were analyzed and compared to chimps, they showed no overall evolutionary pattern of having evolved. The researchers specifically noted, "There is notable lack of positive selection in the coding regions of genes involved in neurogenesis and neural function."[6] So not only were these genes expressed differently, but their DNA sequence did not match the theoretical speculations of evolutionary common descent either—a common theme discussed previously.

Another research project published in 2004 connected differences in brain gene expression with metabolism. The authors stated that "in the ancestry of both humans and chimpanzees, but to a greater extent in humans, are the up-regulated expression profiles of aerobic energy metabolism genes and neuronal function-related genes, suggesting that increased neuronal activity required increased supplies of energy."[7] A more comprehensive study along these lines published in 2010 confirmed the large differences discovered between human and chimp brain gene expression, along with a direct link to metabolic gene data using an even larger set of genes.[6] So, in the grand scheme of evolution, not only would a large number of brain genes have to be controlled differently in humans compared to apes but also numerous other genes involved in cell physiology and metabolism to support the demands of increased brain activity. In support of the complexity of this interconnected genetic data, another research study published in 2011 actually reported that the levels of cell metabolites between human and chimp brains exhibited major differences of 77% in the levels of these metabolic molecules.[8]

If humans actually evolved from apes, then not only would brain genes have changed markedly but also many other genes from multiple interconnected networks associated with both neural and metabolic systems. Of course, this all would have had to evolve in tandem, which is an impossibly complex feat by random mutation and alleged selection.

In 2005, a team of researchers examined gene expression in a variety of different organs between human and chimp.[9] As with the other studies, not only were differences in gene expression highly significant for the brain and even other organs like kidney and liver, but also for the male testes. These results were eventually bolstered by the dramatic differences discovered in the DNA sequence of the Y chromosome between humans and chimps that contain many genes expressed in the testes.

Genes are typically expressed systematically in groups or modules related to various cell functions. Not only is it helpful to look at the expression differences in individual genes or groups of genes, but a more complete picture emerges when we identify overlapping sets and subsets of genes among gene modules. The overlapping subsets of genes common to interconnected modules are termed network connections, just like groups of computers can be connected across large networks. One very interesting study that exploited this idea tested for the similarities and differences in gene module functions between humans and chimps. They found that 17.4% of gene network connections between modules in humans and chimps are completely different.[3] In other words, significant differences existed in the overall network structure of gene modules for many basic cellular physiologies shared between chimps and humans.

One of the most comprehensive studies in human-chimp gene expression was published in 2018 using the most the recent cutting-edge technologies. The authors state, "A comparison between humans and chimpanzees revealed substantial differences in gene expression and CRE [conserved regulatory element] coverage: On average, 12% of genes and 8% of CREs differed significantly between species."[10] In fact, the

researchers were able to connect the genes expressed together in modules and found that many such groups of gene modules were human-specific in their expression. The total number of such genes was found to be very large. The researchers state, "The four human-specific modules representing expression changes in neocortical areas, cerebellum, and hippocampus contained 1851 genes, cumulatively."[10]

Regulatory DNA Differences

Not only are genes regulated in networks and differently between humans and chimps, so are the non-protein-coding sequences in the genome that regulate the genes. In fact, interesting data have also been produced from the analysis of differences in regulatory sequences that are DNA features that control how genes are expressed.

One such study of regulatory DNA sequences compared the control regions of genes called promoters that were similar in human, chimp, and macaque. Promoters are the regions of DNA that immediately precede the gene and play a large role in controlling its level and rate of expression. Of those examined, 575 human gene promoters were found to be markedly different from those in chimps.[11] Many of these promoter differences were associated with genes that control nerve cell development. However, many others were connected to genes associated with more basic metabolic activities like carbohydrate metabolism. Differences in regulatory DNA sequence, even minor variations, can result in large effects.

> "A wide variety of research reports have clearly shown a pattern of incredible irreducible genetic complexity that appears suddenly and fully integrated in humans but is distinctly different from chimpanzees."

Conclusion: Gene Expression Negates Human Evolution

Many genes that represent common code and share sequence similarity between humans and chimps are regulated very differently, and their gene expression profiles bear no signs of common ancestry or make sense in light of theoretical models of evolutionary selection. Genes connected to brain function, cell transport and signaling, testis function, and a variety of metabolic activity show distinctly different expression patterns between humans and chimps. It is also important to note that these genes are positioned within elaborate networks and not only must be precisely coordinated within these genetic systems but also coordinated in their function between organs all over the body. A wide variety of research reports have clearly shown a pattern of incredible irreducible genetic complexity that appears suddenly and fully integrated in humans but is distinctly different from chimpanzees.

References

1. Calarco, J. et al. 2007. Global analysis of alternative splicing differences between humans and chimpanzees. *Genes Development.* 21: 2963-2975.
2. Xiong, J. et al. 2018. Predominant patterns of splicing evolution on human, chimpanzee and macaque evolutionary lineages. *Human Molecular Genetics.* 27: 1474-1485.
3. Oldham, M. C. et al. 2006. Conservation and evolution of gene coexpression networks in human and chimpanzee brains. *Proceedings of the National Academy of Sciences.* 103 (47): 17973-17978.
4. King, M. C. and A. C. Wilson. 1975. Evolution at two levels in humans and chimpanzees. *Science.* 188: 107-116.
5. Cáceres, M. J. et al. 2003. Elevated gene expression levels distinguish human and non-human primate brains. *Proceedings of the National Academy of Sciences.* 100: 13030-13035.
6. Babbitt, C. et al. 2010. Both noncoding and protein-coding RNAs contribute to gene expression evolution in the primate brain. *Genome Biology Evolution.* 2: 67-69.
7. Uddin, M. et al. 2004. Sister grouping of chimpanzees and humans as revealed by genome-wide phylogenetic analysis of brain gene expression profiles. *Proceedings of the National Academy of Sciences.* 101: 2957-2962.
8. Fu, X. et al. 2011. Rapid metabolic evolution in human prefrontal cortex. *Proceedings of the National Academy of Sciences.* 108: 6181-6186.
9. Khaitovich, P. J. et al. 2005. Intra- and Interspecific Variation in Primate Gene Expression Patterns. *Science.* 296: 340-343.
10. Xu, C. et al. 2018. Human-specific features of spatial gene expression and regulation in eight brain regions. *Genome Research.* 28: 1097-1110.
11. Haygood, R. et al. 2007. Promoter regions of many neural- and nutrition-related genes have experienced positive selection during human evolution. *Nature Genetics.* 39: 1140-1144.

10 Human and Chimp Epigenetic Differences

Summary: Genetic tags that make chemical changes to genes are known as epigenetic mechanisms. Epigenetic tags regulate DNA sequence. Studies show that epigenetic differences in human and chimpanzee brain genes are far too great to indicate an evolutionary connection but rather reflect the creature-kind distinctiveness creationists would predict. A study on comparative epigenetics showed orangutans and gorillas had more similar patterns to humans than chimpanzees—a result completely backward to evolutionary predictions.

Epigenetics: The New Frontier

One of the most rapidly advancing and truly exciting fields of research in genetics is the area referred to as epigenetics. The term epigenetics relates to chemical modifications to chromosomes that affect the expression of genes over and above the actual DNA sequence. In epigenetic modifications, the structure and chemistry of the DNA is altered but the actual base pairs that make up the genetic code of DNA stay the same. Epigenetic mechanisms act like separate control codes and systems imposed upon and over the genetic code of DNA sequence. In the study of epigenetic modifications, scientists have linked epigenetics to a wide variety of illnesses, behaviors, and other types of disease associated with cancer, respiratory, autoimmune, cardiovascular, reproductive, and neurobehavioral illnesses.

There are two primary ways in which the DNA of an organism can be modified epigenetically. First, small molecules called methyl groups can be added to the cytosines (C) bases, one of the four letters (A, T, C, G) in the DNA code (Figure 1). Second, protein complexes called histones that the DNA molecule is wrapped around can also be modified in different ways. The various modifications of the histones can make the DNA either more accessible and active or render it inactive. Both of these epigenetic control systems govern how accessible the DNA molecule is to specialized proteins that bind to the DNA and initiate and regulate gene activity (Figure 1). Modification of DNA through these epigenetic systems is dynamically regulated in the genome and plays a huge role in the way that genes are turned on and off. In fact, many human

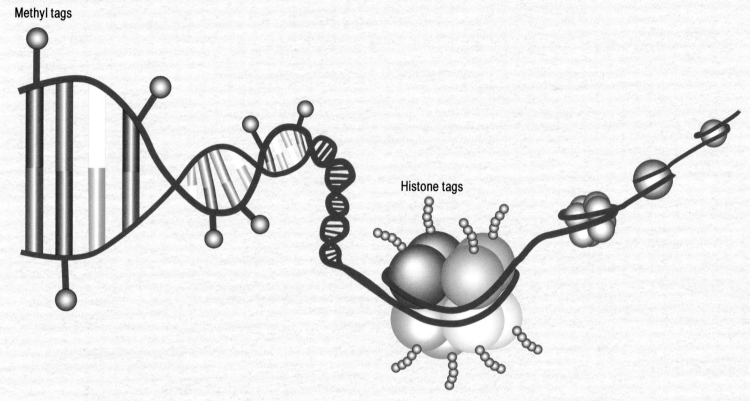

Methyl tags

Histone tags

Figure 1. Depiction of epigenetic modifications in DNA. Methyl tags on cytosine bases in red a and tags on histone proteins are illustrated.

diseases have been associated with aberrant epigenetic alterations that are not part of a normal DNA profile.

Human-Ape Epigenetic Studies Befuddle Evolution

Because evolutionists have speculated that chimpanzees are the closest living relatives to humans, scientists have compared chimp epigenetics to humans in a variety of different types of studies. This research was spurred on by the fact that a number of research reports have shown large differences in gene expression between humans and chimps, as described in the previous chapter. Because epigenetic modifications are directly related to gene expression, scientists have used highly advanced technologies for comparing epigenetic differences between humans and chimps for targeted regions of the genome that they both share.

Using the new tools of genomics, a wide variety of studies quickly showed that dramatic differences existed between humans and chimps in regard to the methylation of cytosine nucleotides as it concerned the regulation of specific genes. One important point to make as we get into this fascinating area of genetics is that the epigenome (the suite of epigenetic modifications) is tissue-specific, and the different patterns vary between the types of cells being studied. The year 2011 seemed to be a banner year for such research, and we will cover three of the top studies that made headlines exposing the dramatic differences between humans and chimps in the area of epigenetics.

One study was performed on purified white blood cells called neutrophils that were taken from living humans, chimps, and orangutans.[1] The researchers chose neutrophils because they are very similar in their appearance and general characteristics between humans and apes. Despite the fact that the most similar type of cell known between humans and apes was selected as a target for study, huge DNA methylation profile differences were found in over 1,500 different areas of the human genome when compared to similar regions of the chimp genomes. Interestingly, the orangutans showed their own uniqueness distinct from humans and chimps in their epigenome.

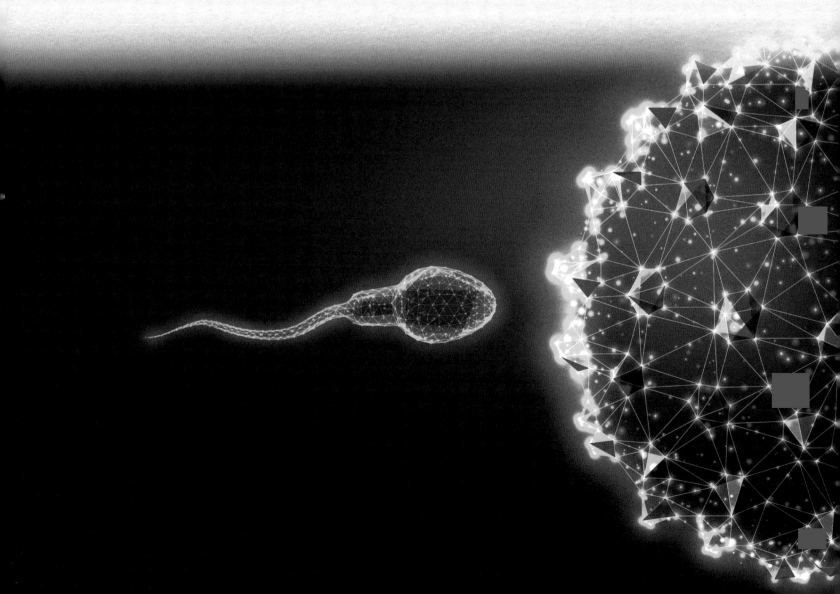

Another important discovery in this research was that epigenetic differences between humans and chimps were not only present in neutrophils but also in the sperm and eggs cells of the germline, indicating that these were heritable differences associated with embryo developmental programs. The authors of the report stated, "The mechanisms leading to the methylation differences between species are unknown. The separate clustering of humans and chimps is consistent with the stable inheritance of methylation states within the two species."[1]

A second study in 2011 evaluated DNA methylation patterns in hearts, livers, and kidneys from multiple humans and chimpanzees, using samples for which gene expression data were also available for 7,723 different genes. This study found "a large number of gene expression differences between species that might be explained, at least in part, by corresponding differences in methylation levels. In particular, we estimate that, in the tissues we studied, inter-species differences in promoter methylation might underlie as much as 12%–18% of differences in gene expression levels between humans and chimpanzees."[2]

In yet another study in 2011, scientists researched the epigenetic modification of the histone proteins that the DNA is packaged around, as mentioned above.[3] Scientists observed significant differences in histone protein modifications in controlling regions of genes between humans and chimps. Their results showed that for the genes they analyzed, differences up to 7% in gene expression between humans and chimps are related to significant differences in specific histone modifications.

A later study in 2012 used an even more specific approach of studying methylation profiles in the DNA surrounding brain genes shared by both humans and chimps. The epigenetic differences found between humans and chimps were strikingly distinct and extensive, as noted by the authors, who said, "We also found extensive species-level divergence in patterns of DNA methylation and that hundreds of genes exhibit significantly lower levels of promoter methylation in the human brain than in the chimpanzee brain."[4]

This study came to the conclusion that these types of brain genes could tolerate very little epigenetic evolutionary modification outside the normal expression profile for the human brain. In fact, the researchers also found that abnormal brain gene methylation patterns are connected with a variety of severe human neurological diseases. These findings demonstrate how methylation changes in brain genes are not well-tolerated, thus negating ideas of these mechanisms allowing human-ape evolution. The research clearly shows that brain gene methylation patterns and their involvement with gene expression are finely tuned and creature kind-specific. The authors of the paper made the following statement regarding this discovery,

> Finally, we found that differentially methylated genes are strikingly enriched with loci associated with neurological disorders, psychological disorders, and cancers.[4]

Another interesting aspect to this research broke down the gene regions affected by epigenetic modifications into different areas. One key gene segment of interest was the promoter region—the regulatory area preceding a gene that controls its function like an on-off switch. The researchers analyzed the main gene body, which is the segment of a gene that includes the protein-coding segments. They also analyzed the tail ends of the genes because they also play a key role in regulation. The human gene promoters were considerably less methylated, an epigenetic state that corresponds to the higher levels of human brain gene activity in contrast to their similar gene counterparts in chimps. In this respect, they discovered that the most dramatic differences between human and chimp brain gene epigenetic patterns were in the control regions, not the gene body. However, the other gene regions also exhibited significant differences but were less dramatic.

> "These findings demonstrate how methylation changes in brain genes are not well-tolerated, thus negating ideas of these mechanisms allowing human-ape evolution."

Overall, 1,055 brain genes showed significantly different epigenetic patterns between humans and chimps. Of these, the researchers found 468 different genes that were highly diverse and played key roles in controlling other genes that regulate processes at the top levels of the cell's system of hierarchy. In other words, the genes that showed the highest levels of differences between humans and chimps were the key regulatory ones for brain cell activity.

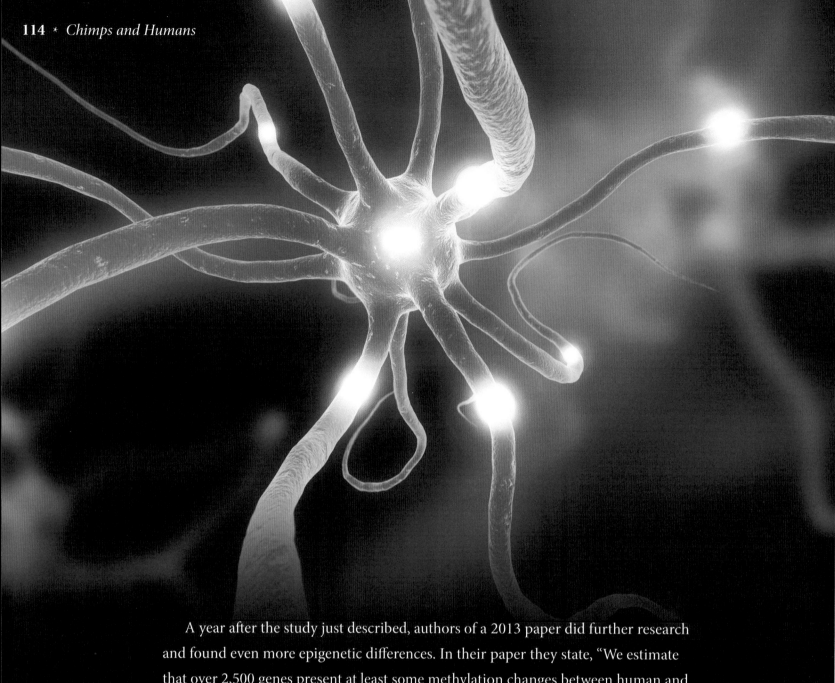

A year after the study just described, authors of a 2013 paper did further research and found even more epigenetic differences. In their paper they state, "We estimate that over 2,500 genes present at least some methylation changes between human and chimpanzees."[5]

And as this type of comparative epigenetics research has become even more advanced, scientists have been able to analyze specific types of brain cells. In 2018, a research study reported that 95% of all compared DNA regions from brain glial cells had different methylation patterns compared to similar regions in the chimp genome.[6] They also found that many of these methylation differences coincided with histone modifications.

Epigenetic Study Produces Backwards Human-Ape Tree

While the DNA code is nearly similar in all cells all over the body, the epigenetic modifications vary depending on the cell and tissue type. Because epigenetic modifications control how genes function in the cell, scientists have been interested in comparing their patterns between humans and apes to determine commonalities and dissimilarities that could be applied to making a more accurate evolutionary tree for human evolution. Along this line of thought, a comparative epigenetic study published by evolutionary scientists completely contradicts the standard inferred evolutionary tree for human-ape evolution.[7]

In this research, scientists analyzed the DNA methylation patterns in the blood cells of humans, chimpanzees, gorillas, and orangutans.[7] The researchers targeted specific areas of chromosomes 21 and 22 that are highly similar among the human and ape genomes. The regions between these two chromosomes that were too dissimilar or less than 98.8% identical were not compared. Comparative epigenetics, like many other types of evolutionary studies based on DNA sequence, can only be performed on the segments of DNA that are highly similar between creatures.

In this particular study, 16 different regions were identified that showed strong DNA methylation pattern differences between humans and chimps. These segments were then targeted for comparison with gorillas and orangutans. These regions were also highly different in their epigenetic patterns between humans and the other apes, but not like those that might be expected based on evolutionary predictions.

When the DNA methylation data from the 16 different areas were used to form an evolutionary tree, it was completely backwards compared to the expected order of common ancestry for apes that supposedly led up to humans (see Figure 2). Orang-

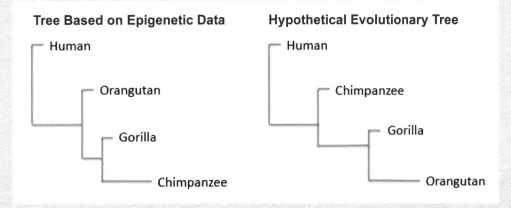

Figure 2. Tree based on data extracted from epigenetic paper.[7] In contrast to tree shown in the paper, differences for chimp and gorilla, compared to human, were 25% greater for chimp—so a more accurate tree depicting this is shown here. The authors misrepresented this fact in their published tree.

utans, who are supposedly the furthest down the evolutionary tree compared to humans, actually had more DNA methylation patterns similar to humans than either chimps or gorillas. And if that was not contradictory enough, gorillas were the next closest in epigenetic similarity to humans, with chimps being the least and falling out last! According to evolution, chimps should have been the most similar to humans, then gorillas, and lastly orangutans. The results produced a backwards evolutionary tree!

While I have documented major differences between human and chimp epigenetics in this chapter, these backwards results are especially interesting because they utterly defy the foundational predictions in the human evolution paradigm—literally turning them upside-down and showing that it's a failed model of human origins.

Human-Ape Epigenetics Summary

Results from DNA regions that are highly similar between humans and chimps show that they have very different epigenetic regulation and only serve to verify the biblical account of creation wherein all forms of life—including humans, chimps, gorillas, and orangutans—were created after their kind. Not only that, but when the epigenetic data are used to create evolutionary trees, the results give a completely mixed-up picture of evolution, producing an evolutionary tree that is entirely backwards. As the Bible says in Psalm 5:10, "Let them fall by their own counsels," and in Psalm 9:16 "The wicked is snared in the work of his own hands."

Once again, research derived from the field of epigenetics profoundly illustrates the distinct genetic differences that exist between humans and apes. As in all the other areas of genetics, the research fits closely with the biblical model that God created all animals "after their kind" (Genesis 1:21) and humans uniquely in the "image of God" (Genesis 1:27).

References
1. Martin, D. I. K. et al. 2011. Phyloepigenomic comparison of great apes reveals a correlation between somatic and germline methylation states. *Genome Research*. 21 (12): 2049-2057.
2. Pai, A. A. et al. 2011. A Genome-Wide Study of DNA Methylation Patterns and Gene Expression Levels in Multiple Human and Chimpanzee Tissues. *PLoS Genetics*. 7 (2): e1001316.
3. Cain, E. C., R. Blekhman, J. C. Marioni, and Y. Gilad. 2011. Gene Expression Differences Among Primates Are Associated With Changes in a Histone Epigenetic Modification. *Genetics*. 187 (4): 1225-1234.
4. Zeng, J. et al. 2012. Divergent Whole-Genome Methylation Maps of Human and Chimpanzee Brains Reveal Epigenetic Basis of Human Regulatory Evolution. *American Journal of Human Genetics*. 91 (3): 455-465.

5. Hernando-Herraez, I. et al. 2013. Dynamics of DNA Methylation in Recent Human and Great Ape Evolution. *PLoS Genetics*. 9 (9): e1003763.

6. Böck, J. et al. 2018. Cell Type and Species-specific Patterns in Neuronal and Non-neuronal Methylomes of Human and Chimpanzee Cortices. *Cerebral Cortex*. 28: 3724-3739.

7. Fukuda, K. et al. 2013. Regional DNA methylation differences between humans and chimpanzees are associated with genetic changes, transcriptional divergence and disease genes. *Journal of Human Genetics*. 58: 446-454.

11 Human and Animal DNA Clocks Verify Recent Creation

Summary: Evolutionists believe genetic mutations progress at a certain rate, and this rate can be used as a type of genetic clock. But studies indicate the rate of genetic mutations—most of which are deleterious—during the production of human sperms and eggs of over 100 mutations per generation is far too rapid to reflect millions of years of evolution. In a process known as genetic entropy, these errors build up over time and indicate the human race is only thousands of years old.

Likewise, mitochondrial DNA and Y chromosome research on a variety of creatures has indicated they were all created less than 10,000 years ago.

Evolutionists believe genetic mutations progress at a certain rate, and this rate can be used as a type of genetic clock. But studies indicate that genetic mutation rates—most of which are deleterious—during the production of human sperm and eggs of over 100 mutations per generation are far too rapid to reflect millions of years of evolution. These errors, known as genetic entropy, build up over time in our population and indicate the human race is only thousands of years old.

Likewise, mitochondrial DNA and Y chromosome research on a variety of creatures has indicated they were all created less than 10,000 years ago.

The Concept of a Genetic Clock

The idea of an evolutionary genetic clock in which DNA sequences steadily change, like a clock ticking off time, has played a major role in the ideas shaping modern biology and theories of human evolution. As typically employed by evolutionists, this theoretical time-measuring technique compares DNA sequences between different species to estimate supposed rates of evolution based on the amount of changes in individual DNA letters (A, T, C, or G) in the DNA. When two totally different types of creatures are compared (e.g., horses and chickens), their differences are made to match up with evolutionary time through a procedure that calibrates the data with deep-time estimates taken from paleontology.[1] While scientists who work in the field know this, the general public is completely unaware of this little trick.

Despite the fact that genetic clock data are clearly manipulated to conform to vast amounts of evolutionary time, the results rarely support the overall evolutionary story. In fact, the following problems are often encountered.

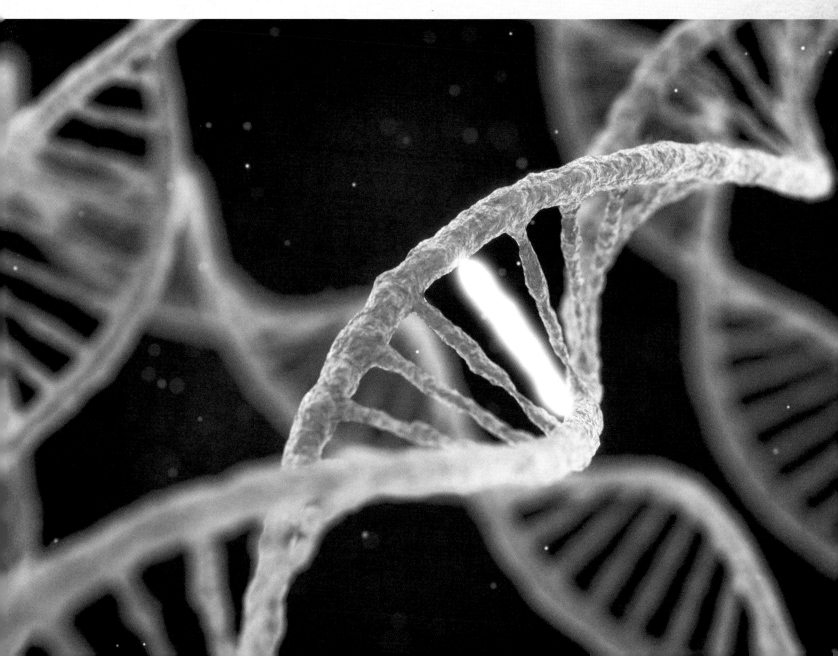

1. Different genes give widely different evolutionary clock rates.
2. Different types of organisms exhibit different rates for the same type of gene sequences.
3. Genetic-clock dates that describe when these creatures supposedly split off to form new creatures (called divergence) commonly disagree with paleontology's timescale despite being calibrated by it.[1]

What kind of data would researchers get if the assumptions of evolution and deep time were not used to bias the molecular-clock models? Would the DNA sequence variation actually provide usable information to help test creationist predictions about origins? Interestingly, we have a variety of reported studies from both secular scientists and creationist researchers in which DNA clocks were measured empirically—without deep-time calibrations—and yielded ages of only 5,000 to 10,000 years, not millions. Each of these test cases are discussed below, but first let's visit the closely related concept of genetic entropy.

Genomic Entropy and Genetic Clocks

During the production of egg and sperm, DNA mutations can occur and be passed on to the next generation. When these are empirically measured within a family's pedigree, an estimate of the mutation rate can be achieved. Scientists have actually measured this rate in humans in a number of studies and found it to be between 75 and 175 mutations per generation.[2-6]

Using this known data about mutation rates, a variety of researchers have used computer simulations to model the accumulation of mutations in the human genome over time.[7-13] It was found that over 90% of mutations fail to be removed over time and are passed on to subsequent generations. Because this buildup of mutations would eventually reach a critical level, it was postulated that humans would eventually go extinct at a point called error catastrophe.[14,15] This continual process of genome degradation over time with each successive generation is called genetic entropy.[14,15] More amazing, the process of genetic entropy is closely mirrored by the trend of declining human life span documented in the Bible, especially in the 4,300 years since the global Flood (Figures 1 and 2).[12,15-17] In addition to these genetic simulation studies, prominent evolutionists have shown that the problem of mutation accumulation in the human genome is accompanied by the inability of natural selection to remove them—an aspect of genetics completely contrary to evolutionary assumptions.[5,18]

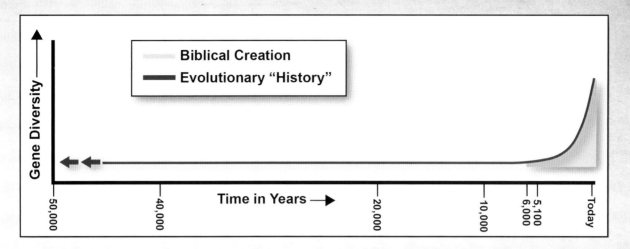

Figure 1. Human genetic population data confirm recent human diversification, shown in blue. The same data confront human evolution's imagined history, shown in red.

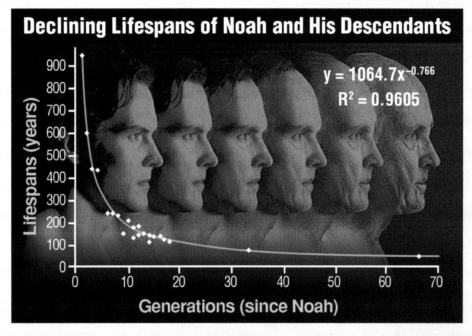

Figure 2. After the Flood, human lifespans quickly began to decline. Image data credit: Sanford, Pamplin, and Rupe.[17]

The conclusions of these studies in modeling genetic entropy have been spectacularly confirmed by two additional secular studies based on empirical data that provided the same results, along with a timescale that paralleled biblical history. Both studies examined the amount of rare single nucleotide differences in the protein-coding regions (exons) of the human genome called the exome.[19,20] One study analyzed 2,440 individuals and the other 6,515. Over 80% of the rare variability was considered to be harmful (associated with heritable disease), and researchers attributed the presence of these mutations to "weak purifying selection."[19] This essentially means that the alleged ability of natural selection to remove these harmful variants from human populations was somehow powerless to do so—the exact same results observed in the computer simulation studies discussed above.[8,11-13]

A major benefit of this type of genetic data is the fact that protein-coding regions are less tolerant of mutation than other parts of the genome, providing more reliable historical genetic information about human populations than more common types of variability. In addition, this type of data can be conveniently integrated into demographic models over known historical time and geographical space. When the researchers did this, they discovered a very recent and massive burst of human genetic diversification primarily associated with genetic entropy. One of the research papers stated, "The maximum likelihood time for accelerated growth was 5,115 years ago."[19] The other paper uncovered a similar timeline, which places the beginning of

Fruit flies

human genetic diversification close to the Genesis Flood and subsequent dispersion of people groups at the Tower of Babel. Importantly, this recent explosion of rare genetic variants clearly associated with genetic entropy also follows the same pattern of human life expectancy rapidly declining after the Flood.[15,17]

Mitochondrial DNA Variability and Genetic Clocks

One other important realm of molecular-clock research demonstrating a recent creation comes from examining mutation rates in mitochondrial genomes.[21] The mitochondrial DNA (mtDNA) of an animal is typically inherited from the mother's egg cell, and the mtDNA mutation rates can accurately be measured in pedigrees to produce a specific clock for that species. When these clocks are calibrated not by evolutionary timescales but by using the organism's known generation time, a more realistic and unbiased estimate of that creature's genetic clock can be obtained. By comparing these mitochondrial clocks in fruit flies, roundworms, water fleas, and humans, one creation scientist demonstrated that a creation event for all of these organisms (including humans) occurred not more than 10,000 years ago.[21]

Mitochondria cell

Other creation scientists also conducted a study into human mtDNA variation in which they statistically analyzed over 800 different sequences and reconstructed a close approximation of Eve's original mitochondrial genome.[15,22] They found that "the average human being is only about 22 mutations removed from the Eve sequence, although some individuals are as much as 100 mutations removed from Eve."[15] The most recent empirical estimate of the mutation rate in human mitochondria is about 0.5 per generation.[23] Based on this rate, even for the most mutated mitochondrial sequences it has been determined that "it would only require 200 generations (less than 6,000 years) to accumulate 100 mutations."[15]

Lest critics say that these mtDNA studies are suspect because they were performed by creationists, it should be noted that evolutionists were actually the first to document these biblically supportive time frames. Buried within a secular research paper back in 1997, the same trends recently observed by creationists regarding human mtDNA mutation rates were first reported but received little attention in the evolutionary community. The authors of the paper stated, "Using our empirical rate to calibrate the mtDNA molecular clock would result in an age of the mtDNA MRCA [most recent common ancestor, or the first human woman] of only ~6,500 years."[24]

One year later, another secular researcher remarked on this study, stating, "Regardless of the cause, evolutionists are most concerned about the effect of a faster mutation rate. For example, researchers have calculated that 'mitochondrial Eve'—the woman whose mtDNA was ancestral to that in all living people—lived 100,000 to 200,000 years ago in Africa. *Using the new clock, she would be a mere 6,000 years old.*"[25]

The article continued to note that the new findings of faster mutation rates pointing to mitochondrial Eve about 6,000 years ago also contributed to the development of mtDNA research guidelines used in forensic investigations adopted by the FBI. Now, over 17 years later, and using even more mtDNA data, creation scientists are spectacularly confirming this previously unheralded discovery.

In addition to the mtDNA clock data, scientists have also analyzed the Y chromosomes of modern men, which they found to be only about 300 mutations on average different from the consensus sequence of a Y-chromosome Adam.[15] The researchers state that "even if we assume a normal mutation rate for the Y chromosome (about 1 mutation per chromosome per generation), we would only need 300 generations (about six thousand years), to get 300 mutations."[15] As with the previous mtDNA work, this is the most straightforward way to apply the DNA clock concept, which also provides data in close agreement with a biblical time frame for the origins of man based on the detailed genealogies and chronologies listed in the Scriptures. Perhaps the most remarkable data supporting a young creation were recently published by a large group of secular scientists who are involved with mapping DNA variation across the entire human genome.[26] This massive effort has just produced a huge data set that the researchers call "a global reference for human genetic variation." In their report, they state:

> Analysis of shared haplotype lengths around f_2 variants suggests a
> median common ancestor ~296 generations ago (7,410 to 8,892 years

ago), although those confined within a population tend to be younger, with a shared common ancestor ~143 generations ago (3,570 to 4,284 years ago).[26]

Amazingly, these are roughly similar dates for both the original creation event and the Babel dispersion after the Flood. The confined populations are descended from the people groups created at the Tower of Babel when the languages became confused. Of course, the median common ancestor of all humans would represent Adam and Eve.

All Life Created Distinctly and Recently

A massive genetic study in 2018 published by secular scientists analyzed the DNA of over 100,000 animal species using about five million DNA sequences.[27] Researchers at The Rockefeller University and the University of Basel found that the amount of DNA variation among humans was about the same as that observed for each of the many animal species they studied. They also discovered that each kind of creature was genetically distinct—having clear genetic boundaries. Study author David Thaler stated, "If individuals are stars, then species are galaxies....They are compact clusters in the vastness of empty sequence space."[28]

> "If individuals are stars, then species are galaxies.... They are compact clusters in the vastness of empty sequence space."

When the researchers extrapolated this data into time frames of origins, they discovered that about 90% of all animal life was roughly the same very recent age—a complete contradiction of evolutionary expectations. Mark Stoeckle, the other study author, remarked, "It is more likely that—at all times in evolution—the animals alive at that point arose relatively recently."[28] According to previous evolutionary reckoning, animals have progressively arisen over a half-billion years—not all at once in recent time.

In a vain attempt to explain these anomalous results, the study authors speculated that somehow life got nearly wiped out across the board about 100,000 to 200,000 years ago and then had to restart.[27] Of course, this is an ad hoc explanation with no corroborative historical evidence.

The only historical record we have of a recent sudden origin of the diversity of life with distinct genetic boundaries (reproducing after their kind) is in the opening chapters of the book of Genesis. The Bible's account is vindicated by science once again.

Clock Conclusion

The evolutionary paradigm of a molecular clock is deeply flawed in that it assumes evolution on a grand scale and literally involves conducting the whole analysis as a hypothetical exercise rather than as an empirical experiment. In contrast, creation scientists and even some secular researchers have taken a straightforward empirical approach without any assumptions about time, and the results yield dates relatively close to a biblical time frame of about 6,000 years. Thus, when the mythical evolutionary restrictions are removed and the data are analyzed empirically, biblical timescales are the result.

References

1. Tomkins, J. P. and J. Bergman. 2015. Evolutionary molecular genetic clocks—a perpetual exercise in futility and failure. *Journal of Creation*. 29 (2): 26-35.
2. Nachman, M. W. and S. L. Crowell. 2000. Estimate of the mutation rate per nucleotide in humans. *Genetics*. 156 (1): 297-304.
3. Kondrashov, A. S. 2003. Direct estimates of human per nucleotide mutation rates at 20 loci causing Mendelian diseases. *Human Mutation*. 21 (1): 12-27.
4. Xue, Y. et al. 2009. Human Y Chromosome Base-Substitution Mutation Rate Measured by Direct Sequencing in a Deep-Rooting Pedigree. *Current Biology*. 19 (17): 1453-1457.
5. Lynch, M. 2010. Rate, molecular spectrum, and consequences of human mutation. *Proceedings of the National Academy of Sciences*. 107 (3): 961-968.
6. Campbell, C. D. and E. E. Eichler. 2013. Properties and rates of germline mutations in humans. *Trends in Genetics*. 29 (10): 575-584.
7. Sanford, J. et al. 2007. Mendel's Accountant: A biologically realistic forward-time population genetics program. *Scalable Computing: Practice and Experience*. 8 (2): 147-165.
8. Sanford, J. et al. 2007. Using Computer Simulation to Understand Mutation Accumulation Dynamics and Genetic Load. *Lecture Notes in Computer Science*. 4488: 386-392.
9. Sanford, J. C. and C. W. Nelson. 2012. The Next Step in Understanding Population Dynamics: Comprehensive Numerical Simulation. *Studies in Population Genetics*. M. C. Fusté, ed. InTech, 117-136.
10. Brewer, W. H., J. R. Baumgardner, and J. C. Sanford. 2013. Using Numerical Simulation to Test the "Mutation-Count" Hypothesis. *Biological Information: New Perspectives*. R. J. Marks III et al, eds. Hackensack, NJ: World Scientific Publishing, 298-311.
11. Gibson, P. et al. 2013. Can Purifying Natural Selection Preserve Biological Information? *Biological Information: New Perspectives*. R. J. Marks III et al, eds. Hackensack, NJ: World Scientific Publishing, 232-263.
12. Nelson, C. W. and J. C. Sanford. 2013. Computational Evolution Experiments Reveal a Net Loss of Genetic Information Despite Selection. *Biological Information: New Perspectives*. R. J. Marks III et al, eds. Hackensack, NJ: World Scientific Publishing, 338-368.
13. Sanford, J. C., J. R. Baumgardner, and W. H. Brewer. 2013. Selection Threshold Severely Constrains Capture of Beneficial Mutations. *Biological Information: New Perspectives*. R. J. Marks III et al, eds. Hackensack, NJ: World Scientific Publishing, 264-297.
14. Sanford, J. 2008. *Genetic Entropy and the Mystery of the Genome*, 3rd ed. Waterloo, NY: FMS Publications.
15. Sanford, J. C. and R. W. Carter. 2014. In Light of Genetics...Adam, Eve, and the Creation/Fall. *Christian Apologetics Journal*. 12 (2): 51-98.
16. Osgood, J. 1981. The Date of Noah's Flood. *Creation*. 4 (1): 10-13.

17. Sanford, J., J. Pamplin, and C. Rupe. Genetic Entropy Recorded in the Bible? FMS Foundation. Posted on kolbecenter.org July 2014.

18. Crow, J. F. 1997. The high spontaneous mutation rate: Is it a health risk? *Proceedings of the National Academy of Sciences*. 94 (16): 8380-8386.

19. Tennessen, J. A. et al. 2012. Evolution and Functional Impact of Rare Coding Variation from Deep Sequencing of Human Exomes. *Science*. 337 (6090): 64-69.

20. Fu, W. et al. 2013. Analysis of 6,515 exomes reveals the recent origin of most human protein-coding variants. *Nature*. 493 (7431): 216-220.

21. Jeanson, N. 2013. Recent, Functionally Diverse Origin for Mitochondrial Genes from ~2700 Metazoan Species. *Answers Research Journal*. 6: 467-501.

22. Carter, R. W. 2007. Mitochondrial diversity within modern human populations. *Nucleic Acids Research*. 35 (9): 3039-3045.

23. Madrigal, L. et al. 2012. High mitochondrial mutation rates estimated from deep-rooting Costa Rican pedigrees. *American Journal of Physical Anthropology*. 148 (3): 327-333.

24. Parsons, T. J. et al. 1997. A high observed substitution rate in the human mitochondrial DNA control region. *Nature Genetics*. 15 (4): 363-368.

25. Gibbons, A. 1998. Calibrating the Mitochondrial Clock. *Science*. 279 (5347): 28-29. Emphasis added.

26. The 1000 Genomes Project Consortium. 2015. A global reference for human genetic variation. *Nature*. 526 (7571): 68-74.

27. Stoeckle, M. Y. and D. S. Thaler. 2018. Why should mitochondria define species? *Human Evolution*. 33 (1-2): 1-30.

28. Hood, M. Sweeping gene survey reveals new facets of evolution. PhysOrg. Posted on phys.org May 28, 2018, accessed July 8, 2018.

12 Dispersion from Babel

Summary: The human evolutionary model describes ape-like ancestors developing in Africa and migrating as modern humans into the rest of the world. But new research shows there is a correlation between global human dispersal and language variation. This matches the Bible's account of the dispersal after the Tower of Babel but is counter to the out-of-Africa theory.

Genetics studies also show that the world's humans can't be divided up into evolutionary races. Rather, they are associated with different nations and language groups as Genesis proclaims.

A key part of the human evolution paradigm is the idea that humans first evolved from ape-like ancestors in Africa and then dispersed across the world from there. Various versions of this scenario exist, but this is the general overall idea. However, the Bible indicates that modern humans derive from Noah's three sons and their wives who survived the global Flood. In addition, the current dispersion and diversity of

people groups around the world is the result of a separation of languages at the Tower of Babel that occurred shortly after the end of the Flood. As we shall see, a wealth of new research in genetics and linguistics is now vindicating the claims of the Bible and debunking the myth of human evolution.

Genetics and Language Analysis Confirm Babel Dispersion

One of the most recent and interesting secular studies lining up with the scriptural account of human origins combined genetics, language, and demographic data. The results also challenge the evolutionary idea of a single lineage of languages and human populations evolving out of Africa.[1] Instead, the data support the idea that multiple people groups have independent origins—a condition one would predict if the confusion of languages at the Tower of Babel happened as described in the Bible.

> "While languages and DNA sequences are passed along differently, they are inextricably linked."

Both language traits and genomic variability in populations change as people migrate to new areas. Some populations split off, and others merge. Thus, while languages and DNA sequences are passed along differently, they are inextricably linked. Because of this fact, combining linguistic and genetic analyses is a logical approach to studying the dispersal of people groups across the earth.

A variety of past studies have analyzed genetic diversity in relation to language for isolated regions of the world such as Europe, India, South and Central America, parts of Africa, etc.,[1] but none have done this on a global scale. Furthermore, earlier studies have been asymmetrical in their strategies when comparing DNA with languages. In other words, some researchers focused on genetic analysis and then used linguistics to interpret the results, while others analyzed linguistic data in the context of genetics. As a result, little is known about global human demographics as determined by combining both genetics and language analyses.

In this fairly recent study, researchers analyzed the largest available data sets of both phonemes (distinct sound units in a language) from 2,082 worldwide languages and genetic profiles from 246 global people groups. The authors of the study stated,

On a global scale, both genetic distance and phonemic distance between populations are significantly correlated with geographic distance," and "there is a relationship between human dispersal and linguistic variation."[1]

Thus, the data used in this rather extensive study helped show how humans have dispersed across the earth, but did the migrations follow evolutionary predictions? The researchers noted, "However, the geographic distribution of phoneme inventory sizes does not follow the predictions of a serial founder effect [single line of descent] during human expansion out of Africa."[1] In other words, there was no clear pattern of dispersal coming out-of-Africa according to popular evolutionary dogma that insists a small group of people first evolved in Africa and then later spread across the world.

While the researchers claimed that the genetic data by itself offered some support for the out-of-Africa hypothesis, they admitted that "genetic and linguistic data show similar signatures of human population dispersal within regions."[1] Both genetic and fossil data are well known to conflict with this popular and scientifically flawed out-of-Africa evolutionary meme.

African savannah sunset

Evolutionary geneticist A. R. Templeton clearly showed that this dogma is bunk in a famous genetic study in which he stated that "the out-of-Africa replacement hypothesis is strongly rejected by the haplotype tree data [genetic-ancestry analyses], and this is also supported by the fossil and current human data."[2] So clearly this recent study, taken as a whole, matches up with the well-supported fact that people groups have multiple points of origins. But are these evolutionary points of origins?

The Bible teaches that shortly after the Flood, mankind disobeyed God's commandment to replenish and fill the earth. Instead, they stayed in one place and attempted to re-establish the same pre-Flood pagan culture that had originally filled the earth with violence and wickedness and brought about God's judgment. Therefore, God confused their common language and brought an end to their centralized rebellious ambitions, forcing them to split off into different people groups (Genesis 11). This ultimately led to the diversity among nations and people groups that we see today—a multiple origins model based on the Bible that fits perfectly with the scientific data.

Skin Color Research Confirms Biblical Narrative

People over the ages have placed great emphasis on race and skin color. Eugenicist-minded Darwinists have used it as the basis for much ill-conceived mischief.[3] Even Darwin himself proposed that darker-skinned human populations were more primitive. However, we now know that all people groups share the same basic genome comprised of a well-documented set of common genetic variants. Darwin was mistaken—no people group is more primitive than another.

Additionally, the rare genetic variants that arose via random mutation and are mostly associated with human disease and degeneration show that the current state of the human genome cannot be more than about 5,000 years old, as discussed in the previous

> "Darwin was mistaken—no people group is more primitive than another."

chapter. This time frame matches up with the world being repopulated after the global Flood by Noah's sons and their wives.[4-7]

Despite our increasing knowledge of the human genome, little is known about the genetic basis of skin color. Up until now, most of what scientists understood about skin color genetics came from research using European people groups. Researchers originally discovered that variations in a gene called *SLC24A5* influenced skin cells to produce less pigment. This appeared to provide a basis for pale skin.[8] However, this single gene was only a small part of a much more complex trait.

To more fully explain the genetic basis of human skin color variation, a group of researchers recently went to Africa—the most genetically diverse continent on Earth.[9] Contrary to conventional thought, Africa contains a huge amount of variation in human skin color across its different people groups. To scientifically measure the variation in skin color, the researchers measured light reflectance from the skin on the underside of the wrists of 2,092 people in the countries of Ethiopia, Tanzania, and Botswana. This area's skin is largely protected from sunlight, and these readings provide a good indirect estimate of pigmentation levels (skin color). Then the researchers analyzed the DNA of 1,570 of these individuals for genetic variation in their genomes related to skin color.

The scientists identified four major regions of the human genome that contained six different genes. Together, these genes accounted for about 30% of the observed skin color variation. The study reported on DNA variants associated with light skin and variants causing dark skin, both of which are abundant in the African populations. The genetic variant causing light skin is commonly present in East Africans, but this doesn't necessarily mean they will have light skin because multiple genes interact with each other to determine skin color. These results countered the long-held evolutionary belief that the original ancestral humans in Africa were all once dark-skinned.

This line of research has

Woman from Botswana

even broader global implications. For example, it shows that other dark-skinned people in southern India, Australia, and New Guinea did not somehow separately develop their skin color because the mystical forces of evolution favored it. They simply inherited the already existing ancestral dark variants as people groups dispersed around the world. And while evolutionists are constantly debating where and how humans actually dispersed after they supposedly evolved, the Bible indicates that human global migration happened shortly after the global Flood at the Tower of Babel when God confused their languages and forced them to disperse.

Not-So-Simple Human Traits Validate Babel Dispersion

Many people were told in biology class that some basic human traits reflect simple genetic principles. One example is how earlobes are attached. When I was in high school, our biology teacher told us to examine each other's ears and see how many had attached versus unattached earlobes. Attached earlobes do not have a lobe that dangles. In general, there were many more students with unattached than attached earlobes. We were told the attached variant is an example of a classic single-gene recessive trait, an explanation that makes genetics appear overly simple.

However, some scientists have been questioning this oversimplified paradigm since well before the days of modern genomics and DNA analysis. As early as 1937, one scientist pointed out that earlobe attachment could be a multi-gene trait.[10] Thanks to modern research techniques that help reveal the mysteries of the genome, we now know that even the concept of what clearly defines a single gene is blurred by unimaginable and unexpected complexity.[11] A recent research report on the classic textbook idea that a single gene controls earlobe attachment has once again reached the standard conclusion of the genomics era—genetic activity appears to be far more complex than previously thought.

In this earlobe genetics study, researchers used DNA sequencing data and earlobe measurements from 74,660 people with European, Latin American, or Chinese ancestry. By associating DNA sequences across the genome with the ear development patterns in people, the researchers identified 49 genomic regions related to the attached earlobe trait. They also sequenced the products of genes turned on during ear development, which confirmed that the many different genes they discovered in their DNA trait association study were in fact located among many different associated regions in the genome. The authors of the paper state, "These genes provide insight into the complex biology of ear development."[12]

This study followed closely on the heels of two other human genetics studies that debunk the previously held belief that skin color is controlled by only a few major genes.[13,14] Both studies used human subjects from countries in Africa, the continent with the largest spectrum of skin color diversity in the world. One study found that six major genes contribute to 30% of the total variability in skin color.[14,15] The other 70% of the genetic contribution to color variability was from numerous other genes and regions around the genome.

The oversimplified evolutionary paradigm does not fit well with human genome studies that consistently show ever-increasing levels of complexity. Seemingly simple traits turn out to be not simple at all due to the networked interconnectivity of genes in complex dynamic systems throughout the genome. Only an all-wise Creator could be responsible for engineering these amazing systems.

The genetic complexity of traits like skin color allows for all of the amazing diversity we see in humans today. An example of how quickly and easily skin color can manifest is spectacularly illustrated by the birth of twins to a couple in England. The father was a very light-skinned European, while the mother was dark-skinned and of Jamaican-African descent. The couple has three children that have shades of skin color in between. But interestingly, they also had a set of twins. One had extremely pale, light skin with red, straight hair, while the other had dark skin and dark, curly hair. This striking example shows how quickly diversity in humans can arise from the same genetic stock. Clearly, the original Adam and Eve couple, and then later Noah's sons and their wives, had all of the genetic diversity needed to produce the variety we see today among humans the world over.

Mitochondrial DNA Confirms Noah's Sons in Human Ancestry

As discussed in the previous chapter, humans inherit from their mothers a small circular piece of DNA inside their cell's mitochondria. This mitochondrial DNA is an excellent tool for tracing genetic ancestry. By studying the mitochondrial DNA sequence of thousands of humans from all over the world deposited in public databases, creation scientist Nathaniel Jeanson has not only shown that the mutations in this DNA indicate a very recent creation, but he has also found proof of the genetic bottleneck of the Flood.[16] When Jeanson arranged these sequences by similarity into a tree using a highly sophisticated algorithm, he discovered three main nodes or branch points corresponding to points of genetic origin. Noah's sons and their wives formed the genetic pool for the repopulation of the world. The mitochondrial DNA results correspond perfectly with this key biblical truth.

"He has made from one blood every nation of men to dwell on all the face of the earth."

Conclusion

Instead of humans being divided up into so-called races accordingly to an evolutionary mindset, the Bible talks about different peoples being associated with different nations and language groups. As we all know, people from different regions and cultures around the world can look quite different. Evolution has few answers as to how these differences occurred, but the Bible does. The apostle Paul stated in Acts 17:26, "He has made from one blood every nation of men to dwell on all the face of the earth." And we also know that this one blood or original Adam and Eve genome went through a genetic bottleneck through the Flood, along with a confusion of languages shortly thereafter. Amazingly, genetics and lingusitics data both fully vindicate the Scriptures.

References
1. Creanza, N. et al. 2015. A comparison of worldwide phonemic and genetic variation in human populations. *Proceedings of the National Academy of Sciences.* 112: 1265-1272.
2. Templeton, A. R. 2005. Haplotype Trees and Modern Human Origins. *Yearbook of Physical Anthropology.* 48: 33–59.

3. Bergman, J. 2014. *The Darwin Effect*. Green Forest, AR: Master Books.

4. Tomkins, J. P. Human DNA Variation Linked to Biblical Event Timeline. *Creation Science Update*. Posted on ICR.org July 23, 2012, accessed October 13, 2017.

5. Tomkins, J. P. Genetics Research Confirms Biblical Timeline. *Creation Science Update*. Posted on ICR.org January 9, 2013, accessed October 13, 2017.

6. Tomkins, J. P. 2014. Genetic Entropy Points to a Young Creation. *Acts & Facts*. 43 (11): 16.

7. Tomkins, J. P. 2015. Genetic Clocks Verify Recent Creation. *Acts & Facts*. 44 (12): 9-11.

8. Sturm, R. A. 2009. Molecular genetics of human pigmentation diversity. *Human Molecular Genetics*. 18 (R1): R9–R17.

9. Crawford, N. G. et al. 2017. Loci associated with skin pigmentation identified in African populations. *Science*. 358 (6365): eaan8433.

10. Wiener, A. S. 1937. Complications in ear genetics. *Journal of Heredity*. 28 (12): 425-426.

11. Tomkins, J. P. 2014. Gene Complexity Eludes a Simple Definition. *Acts & Facts*. 43 (6): 9.

12. Shaffer, J. R. et al. 2017. Multiethnic GWAS Reveals Polygenic Architecture of Earlobe Attachment. *American Journal of Human Genetics*. 101 (6): 913-924.

13. Crawford, N. G. et al. 2017. Loci associated with skin pigmentation identified in African populations. *Science*. 358 (6365): eaan8433.

14. Martin, A. R. et al. 2017. An Unexpectedly Complex Architecture for Skin Pigmentation in Africans. *Cell*. 171 (6): 1340-1353.

15. Tomkins, J. P. Skin Color Research Confirms Biblical Narrative. *Creation Science Update*. Posted on ICR.org November 2, 2017, accessed December 4, 2017.

16. Jeanson, N. T. 2016. On the Origin of Human Mitochondrial DNA Differences, New Generation Time Data Both Suggest a Unified Young-Earth Creation Model and Challenge the Evolutionary Out-of-Africa Model. *Answers Research Journal*. 9: 123-130.

13 Conclusion and Implications

Summary: Recent research fully supports a literal and historical Adam and Eve. Rapid genetic entropy in humans points to an original pristine genome only thousands of years ago. Human and chimps aren't nearly as genetically close as evolutionists once claimed. Recent genetics research shows that humans and other creatures were created according to their kind just as the Bible clearly describes. The Bible's narrative of human origins is true and historically and scientifically defendable.

The Evolutionary Problem of Human-Chimp Discontinuity

Many evolutionists have claimed over the past four decades that the DNA of humans and chimps is nearly identical. However, as has been demonstrated in this book, an ever-increasing amount of data from diverse disciplines in the field of genetics strongly challenges the dogma that humans are just a few DNA base pairs short of being a monkey. Unfortunately, your typical popular media science journalist will usually sensationalize and misrepresent new research and be blissfully ignorant of the studies that negate human evolution. Adding to this media bias, many researchers are guilty of omitting, discarding, filtering, and manipulating genetic data to produce results that are considerably more favorable

> **"The real truth about human-chimp DNA nonsimilarity and the huge genetic chasm that exists between us and apes rarely makes its way to the general public."**

to the evolutionary paradigm, as I have discussed in this book. Therefore, the real truth about human-chimp DNA nonsimilarity and the huge genetic chasm that exists between us and apes rarely makes its way to the general public.

The glaring reality is the opposite of evolution—our genomes are not evolving but instead are devolving and becoming more degenerate with time. Genetic information follows a historical pattern of corruption through mutation and entropy over time. In fact, within the span of embryo development to elderly adulthood, a single person will rack up more than 2,000 mutations in their DNA per cell in their body.[1,2] The mutations that occur in the cells leading to the production of egg and sperm are passed on to one's offspring. As discussed in an earlier chapter, the human genome as studied from DNA samples taken from thousands of people the world over actually illustrates these signs of decay based on the accumulation of harmful mutations. These data indicate a creation-based starting point that was originally pristine. Clearly, we have been sold a false bill of evolutionary goods by the popular media and secular scientists.

The Concept of Limited Similarity

So, what is the actual amount of DNA similarity between the human and chimp genomes, and when does this level of similarity become some sort of official level of discontinuity? Unfortunately, unbiased whole genome comparisons between human and chimpanzee are remarkably lacking, and many comparisons that have been made discard large amounts of data that do not match up well or are not similar. In fact, the majority of publications have only reported genetic and functional similarities on the most highly identical protein-coding genes.

A key dogma of the evolutionary model is the idea that human DNA and chimpanzee DNA are 98.5% identical. This level of DNA similarity is needed to support the hypothetical idea that humans and chimps shared a common ancestor three to six million years ago. Based on known mutation rates in both humans and chimps and the amount of change that could have occurred over three to six million years, anything significantly less than a 98.5% DNA identity would destroy the foundation of the entire theory.

As I studied the scientific literature on the subject of human-chimp DNA similarity, I realized there were serious problems with the evolutionary idea of pervasive nearly identical human and chimp DNA. In every research publication I examined, it became clear scientists had cherry-picked highly similar DNA sequences that supported evolution and discarded the data that were dissimilar.[3] In six of the top papers, I recalculated DNA similarities by factoring back in omitted data and obtained much lower levels of human-chimp DNA similarity, between 66% and 86%. The general consensus was that at maximum, overall human-chimp DNA similarity did not exceed 86%—an amount that my own research and that of others would soon prove.

Aside from the evolutionary DNA similarity shenanigans, another major issue I uncovered is that the chimpanzee genome was literally put together to resemble the human genome.[4-6] This little-known fact was accomplished by taking the small snippets of DNA produced after sequencing and lining them up on the human genome. The human genome guided the researchers throughout the chimp genome assemblage process.

Despite these issues brought about because of scientists' evolutionary bias, continuing improvement in DNA sequencing technology is slowly bringing the truth to light. The newest version of the chimpanzee genome was recently completed, and the results not only validate my own research but also spectacularly confirm research I published in 2018.[6,7]

The research paper for the new chimp genome, called PanTro6, completely side-steps the issue of DNA similarity with humans.[7] Nevertheless, University of London evolutionist Richard Buggs analyzed the results of a comprehensive comparison of the new chimp genome with the human one and posted his shocking anti-evolutionary findings. He stated, "The percentage of nucleotides in the human genome that had one-to-one exact matches in the chimpanzee genome was 84.38%."[8]

What makes Buggs' analysis more amazing is the fact that my own published research using results derived from a different algorithm gave a similar outcome. In my study, I aligned 18,000 random pieces of high-quality chimp DNA about 31,000 DNA letters long (on average) onto human and several different versions of the chimp genome.[6,9] Not only did my data show that the older version of the chimp genome (PanTro4) that had been used to support evolution was deeply flawed and humanized, but they also showed the aligned segments of chimp DNA were on average only 84% identical to human—the same level of similarity reported by Buggs.

These new results by both myself and Buggs also closely match a 2016 study I published that indicated the overall human-chimp DNA similarity was likely no more than 85%.[5] Based on the most recent research, the difference between the human and chimp genomes is estimated to be about 16%, and likely more.

A 16% DNA difference between humans and chimps is a discrepancy that can't be ignored when no more than about a 1 to 2% difference is required to make human evolution seem at all plausible. While some level of similarity is to be expected among humans and apes because we share similar gross morphologies and physiologies, the genomes are clearly very different and unique.

Some people might still say, however, "Isn't 84% DNA similarity still a lot, and what does that mean?" The answer to that question is really quite simple. First, we must recognize that DNA is a type of code. A good analogy would be the computer code that is enigineered by humans. Common code can exist between different computer programs that have completely different purposes, but they contain similar code because the same type of functions are being called upon. In fact, both humans and apes have similar physiologies and even gross similarities in overall body plans, so one would expect many similarities to a great extent in their DNA. From a biblical design-based perspective, this design signature, along with evidence of genetic discontinuity (reproducing only after their kind), is a fundamental part of the creation model. The scientific accuracy of the Bible is vindicated regarding the uniqueness of humans as stated in Genesis 1:27: "So God created man in His own image; in the image of God He created him; male and female He created them."

Moral Implications of Humans as Evolved Apes

As I have shown, scientific research regarding the issue of human origins has been purposefully skewed to promote and establish a secular agenda of evolution along with the unspoken implications of human degradation. The moral, or rather amoral, aspects of humans being regarded as nothing more than just variants of another evolved animal are dangerous.

By dehumanizing people, many malicious inventions aimed at societal and population control can be justified by the ungodly controlling elements of our modern society that are dominated by people with a devout anti-human mindset. While it is not the purpose of this book to delve into the geopolitical issues of our time, one recent well-researched book on this subject has shown how a dehumanizing "Scientific Technocracy" has been steadily growing the world over.[10] This is one key reason why the issue of human origins is so important to understand.

One of the foundational paradigms of the technocratic establishment in their campaign to dehumanize is the idea that humans share a common ancestry with apes and that therefore we have no more value than any other animal. Outward manifestations of this dehumanizing paradigm are abortion, eugenics, and euthanasia.

Trans-Humanist-Directed Evolution of Man

The increasingly popular idea that humans are able to further evolve to a new level or even become a new species with the mandated help of the "experts" has been proposed by a number of prominent evolutionary technocrats such as Ray Kurzweil.[11] In fact, you may have heard of this area of both research and thinking called trans-humanism.

This trans-humanist agenda is typically portrayed as a positive trend and incorporates a diversity of technologies such as genetic modification of the human genome, implantable electronic devices, exotic new designer drugs, specialized vaccines, and various other biological enhancements to the human body. One of the central paradigms of trans-humanism is the goal of merging man and machine.

The twisted logic behind the trans-humanist paradigm is that many of these new technologies will help "fix" the mistakes of evolution and move us to the next evolutionary level of human advancement. However, given the sinful nature of unregenerate mankind, the reality is that while this technology might be used to improve the quality of life for some handicapped people, the deployment of it on a broad scale to the general public would likely be nefarious in the end.

Importance of a Literal Adam

Many Christians may claim that the biblical account of a literal Adam along with the issue of human evolution are not directly related to the mission of Jesus Christ in redemption and that we should not be overly concerned about it, but this is simply not true. Not only are humans created uniquely in the image of God, but the story of a literal historical Adam is central to the gospel of Jesus Christ. Through a literal Adam and Eve ancestral couple, sin entered into the world, along with death, misery, and corruption, which accounts for the central problem of evil in the world. Roman 5:12 says, "Therefore, just as through one man sin entered the world, and death through sin, and thus death spread to all men, because all sinned," and Romans 5:17 states, "For if by the one man's offense death reigned through the one, much more those who receive abundance of grace and of the gift of righteousness will reign in life through the One, Jesus Christ." We also have this foundational gospel truth repeated in 1 Corinthians 15:22, which says, "For as in Adam all die, even so in Christ all shall be made alive."

Of course, Jesus Christ, the very author of our salvation, affirmed the historicity of a literal human couple by saying in Matthew 19:4, "Have you not read that He who made them at the beginning made them male and female?" The Lord Jesus Christ not only confirmed the historicity of the original created human couple but also that this occurred at the very beginning of creation. And we know from detailed genealogies throughout the Bible, combined with chronological data on times of birth and death, that the earth is approximately 6,000 years old. And as described in an earlier chapter,

empirically derived genetic clocks confirm a young age for the origin of mankind and the animals. The secular idea that after billions of years of primeval history followed by millions of years of human-ape evolution, modern humans somehow emerged is completely unbiblical and also unsupported by sound science.

> **"I am fearfully and wonderfully made."**

Final Conclusion

While evolutionists have ardently labored to prove their model for the naturalistic origins of mankind, their ill-guided quest has increasingly failed. The continuing outcome of modern genetics and genomics research has done nothing but provide copious amounts of scientific data that fully support the biblical model that mankind was created uniquely in the image of God as described in the opening chapters of Genesis. When the origins of mankind are viewed in this light, along with the story of mankind's original rebellion, the problem of evil in the world and our need for new life and redemption in Christ Jesus become crystal clear.

The Bible also states in Psalm 139:14, "I am fearfully and wonderfully made; Marvelous are Your works." From a sound-minded Christian perspective, the concept of man created uniquely as described in the book of Genesis has profound theological and practical considerations for daily Christian living. If the biblical narrative of mankind's origins in the book of Genesis is true, which science now fully supports, then we can believe and trust in the other parts of the Bible as well.

References

1. Bae, T. et al. 2017. Different mutational rates and mechanisms in human cells at pregastrulation and neurogenesis. *Science*. 359 (6375): 550-555.
2. Lodato, M. A. et al. 2017. Aging and neurodegeneration are associated with increased mutations in single human neurons. *Science*. 359 (6375): 555-559.
3. Tomkins, J. and J. Bergman. 2012. Genomic monkey business—estimates of nearly identical human-chimp DNA similarity re-evaluated using omitted data. *Journal of Creation*. 26 (1): 94-100.
4. Tomkins, J. 2011. How genomes are sequenced and why it matters: implications for studies in comparative genomics of humans and chimpanzees. *Answers Research Journal*. 4: 81-88.
5. Tomkins, J. 2016. Analysis of 101 Chimpanzee Trace Read Data Sets: Assessment of Their Overall Similarity to Human and Possible Contamination With Human DNA. *Answers Research Journal*. 9: 294-298
6. Tomkins, J. 2018. Comparison of 18,000 De Novo Assembled Chimpanzee Contigs to the Human Genome Yields Average BLASTN Alignment Identities of 84%. *Answers Research Journal*. 11: 215-219.
7. Kronenberg, Z. N. et al. 2018. High-resolution comparative analysis of great ape genomes. *Science*. 360 (6393): eaar6343.
8. Buggs, R. How similar are human and chimpanzee genomes? Posted on richardbuggs.com July 14, 2018, accessed August 9, 2018.
9. Tomkins, J. P. 2018. Separate Studies Converge on Human-Chimp DNA Dissimilarity. *Acts & Facts* 47 (11): 9.
10. Collins, P. D. and P. D. Collins. 2006. *The Ascendancy of the Scientific Dictatorship: An Examination of Epistemic Autocracy, From the 19th to the 20th Century*. Charleston, SC: BookSurge Publishing.
11. Kurzweil, R. 2005. *The singularity is near: when humans transcend biology*. New York: Viking Press.

A Appendix
DNA and Genome Primer

How DNA and Genes Work

The central information command center of plant and animal cells is the nucleus, a specialized cellular compartment that contains the genetic information and accompanying machinery that provide the instructions and information processing tools required to build and maintain cells, tissues, and whole bodies. The genetic information is contained in the chromosomes, which are composed of deoxyribonucleic acid (DNA) in highly specified chains of nucleotide molecules. The order of nucleotides specifies a wide variety of encoded information. Some of this code is regulatory in nature, while other areas contain specific information that contains information to make proteins. A specific region of the DNA that contains information for a protein or a functional RNA molecule is called a gene.

The genetic code itself is determined by the order of the four nucleotide molecules in the DNA: adenine (A), thymine (T), guanine (G), and cytosine (C). These four nucleotides are chemically connected together in a long chains by a sugar (deoxyribose) phosphate backbone. Even more amazing is the fact that the DNA molecule exists as a long double-stranded molecule. The opposing strands are paired up like a zipper through a process called complementary base-pairing. In DNA base-pairing, A's pair with T's and C's pair with G's via a weak nonchemical connection called hydrogen bonding.

Even though hydrogen bonds are not a strong type of bonding that involves actual chemical changes, the molecular attractions are forceful enough to keep the DNA double-stranded molecule stable, like a big zipper. These weak bonds between complementary paired nucleotides, however, are not so strong as to prevent specified cell machinery from "unzipping" the DNA during gene expression and DNA replication. The exact nature and perfectly designed level of strength in the hydrogen bonds of

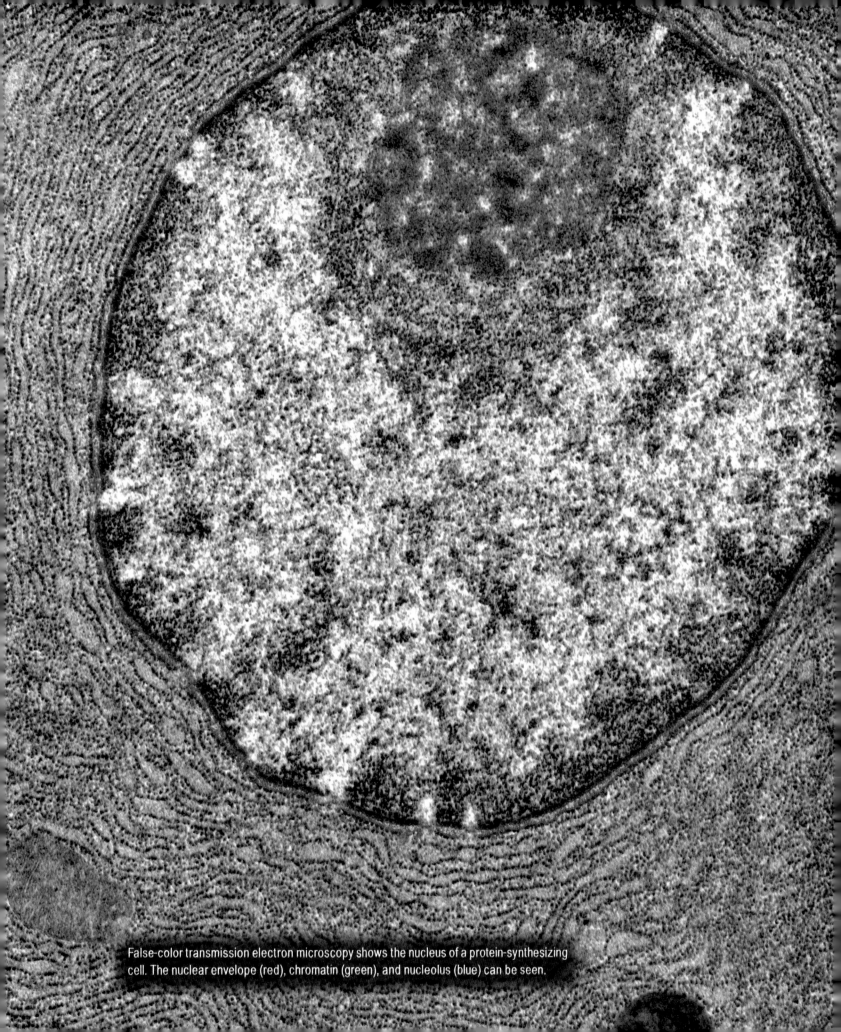

False-color transmission electron microscopy shows the nucleus of a protein-synthesizing cell. The nuclear envelope (red), chromatin (green), and nucleolus (blue) can be seen.

paired bases allows the precise function of DNA required for many different cellular processes.

The DNA sequence of chromosomes is the principle information storage component of the cell's system and is exquisitely interconnected with the signaling and control circuitry of the cell. When the manufacture of a protein or suite of proteins is required, genes become activated in the nucleus by a complicated array of molecular machinery. Copies of the gene's protein-coding sequences are produced in a process called transcription, which results in a transcript called a messenger RNA (mRNA).

Transcription of genes is initiated by specialized proteins that bind to and activate the genes in specific areas of DNA sequence called regulatory regions. Many of these regulatory features in the DNA are positioned in front of the gene or at its beginning in regions called promoters. The activating regulatory proteins that engage promoters are called transcription factors. The binding of the transcription factors turns genes on or off, thus initiating or stopping transcription. Gene regulatory features also modulate

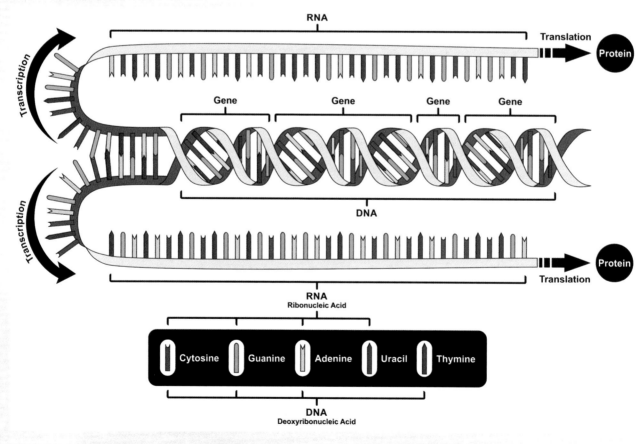

This image depicts the general features of information storage in living cells. RNA and DNA consist of chemical bases such as cytosine arranged according to a language called the genetic code. DNA stores the information, and RNA helps convey that information to cellular machinery that then translates the code into thousands of unique proteins.

the rates and levels of transcription. Besides promoters, there are other specific DNA sequence features throughout the length of the gene that also modulate transcription and how the transcripts are processed after transcription. The overall process and orchestrated aspects of gene expression are tightly regulated, very complicated, and irreducibly complex in every respect.

Technological advances in laboratory-based robotics and automation have not only increased the ability to determine the sequence of DNA but have provided scientists the ability to analyze thousands of genes and their expression patterns in just a few experiments. This type of research has been termed functional genomics and is revealing that genes are regulated in incredibly complex interconnected networks.

When a gene is turned on for some purpose in the cell, a specialized machine called an RNA polymerase (large protein complex) starts the process of copying the gene termed transcription. An RNA transcript or an mRNA is produced and may be used as a template for a protein or used directly as a functional or structural RNA in some way. The main difference between RNA and DNA is that a slightly different type of sugar molecule is used in connecting the RNAs called a ribose, and the nucleotide base uracil (U) substitutes for thymine (T). In addition, the resulting mRNA transcript is composed of a single strand whereas the DNA of chromosomes are double-stranded.

The information content to make a protein in the encoded message in DNA and the subsequent RNA transcript is based on the order of three consecutive nucleotide bases called a codon. Each codon specifies one of 20 different amino acids. These codons translate into a specific protein that is a chain of amino acids. This process of chaining together amino acids based on an RNA template occurs outside the nucleus at specialized machinery called ribosomes in a process called translation.

Prior to the translation process, the RNA transcript has to be processed in various ways. Specialized protein complexes edit, remove, and add a variety of features to the RNA transcript in a highly controlled and regulated series of steps called post-transcriptional processing and modification.

In humans, animals, and plants, genes are engineered in pieces where the coding sections called exons are interrupted by noncoding segments called introns. In many cases, introns are actually longer than exons. The number of exons in a gene can be highly variable and ranges from one to over 100 depending on the type of gene. When an RNA is first copied from a gene, the transcript initially includes both exon and intron sequence and is called a pre-mRNA. Shortly after transcription, the pre-mRNA undergoes the removal of intron sequences, the possible removal of some exons, and even the possible addition of exons from other transcripts. The RNA transcript can also be changed by the literal altering of its code on the fly in a process called RNA editing. The selection and adding of exons creates the ability to form a large variety of mRNAs from a single gene in a process called alternative splicing. It is now believed that over 90% of genes in humans employ alternative splicing.

When the structure of genes was first being discovered in the 1970s and 1980s, scientists were baffled by what they found, and because of their ignorance they initially thought that the noncoding intron sequences along with many areas in between genes served no discernable function. In fact, they immediately labeled them as useless remnants of random evolutionary processes which fostered the use of the term junk DNA. However, extensive research in the human genome project has shown that the introns inside genes contain many important regulatory signal sequences that control transcription and splicing events. Some introns even code for RNAs that participate in the process of RNA splicing and other critical aspects of gene expression. Even the extensive regions between protein-coding genes contain many other genes that code for long functional RNAs, as well as numerous control regions that affect gene regulation.

When the processing of a newly transcribed RNA is complete, the final product is chaperoned out of the nucleus through a specialized portal in the nuclear membrane. The RNA is then guided through the cytoplasm to a ribosome where translation of a protein takes place. Ribosomes are large complicated protein machines that rapidly and efficiently perform the polymerization of amino acids by decoding the codons of an RNA and connecting the correct amino acid in sequence accordingly.

The final protein that is produced is not simply a linear chain of amino acids but a highly specified three-dimensional structure that is folded and shaped with the help of other proteins based on its intended purpose and function. In many instances, proteins are also modified by the addition of metal ions or sugar molecules, and even complexed with other proteins.

For the most part, proteins enable the majority of work in the cell during daily

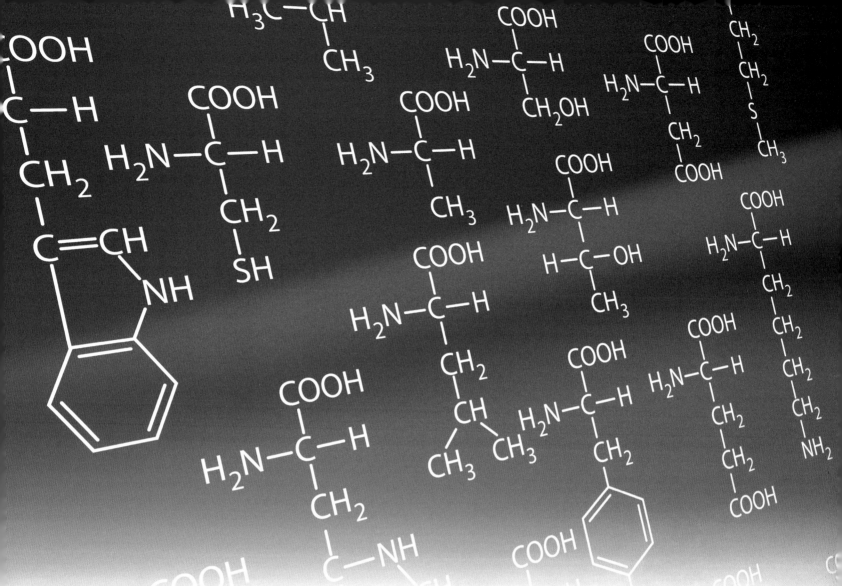

physiology, growth, and development. Proteins also provide the basis of many structural features in the cell and in bodily tissues. There are many different types of proteins, and the huge diversity of protein biochemistry is mind-boggling.

Genomes and Genomics

An organism's genome is a scientific term that is becoming much more common, and it refers to the set of chromosomes that are located in the nucleus of animal and plant cells. In contrast, bacteria do not have a nucleus, and their genome is located in the cytoplasm and is usually found in the form of a circular chromosome.

Genomes in animals and plants are typically referred to in single sets. In humans, there are two genomes present in nearly every cell—one from your father and one from your mother. A single human genome complement is 23 chromosomes and consists of about three billion base pairs of DNA. Because we have two sets of chromosomes, we have 46 in total, with six billion base pairs of DNA per cell. Two of the 46 chromosomes are sex chromosomes that contain genes for specifying and maintaining male and female traits and are called the X and Y chromosomes. Males have an XY configuration, with the Y being the male-specifying chromosome. Females have an XX chromosome complement, with one of the two X chromosomes being shut down to eliminate apparent dosage effects from the genes on both X chromosomes. All the other non-sex chromosomes are called autosomes.

In the cell's cytoplasm outside the nucleus are membrane-bound specialized compartments (organelles) called mitochondria that are the energy-making factories in the cell. The mitochondria contain a small circular DNA molecule of about 16,000 base pairs that provides a portion of the genes needed for energy metabolism. This small piece of DNA is called the mitochondrial genome. The mitochondrial DNA is mostly inherited from a person's mother through her egg cell. However, when scientists discuss the genome in a general sense, it is typically the DNA in the nucleus that is being referred to.

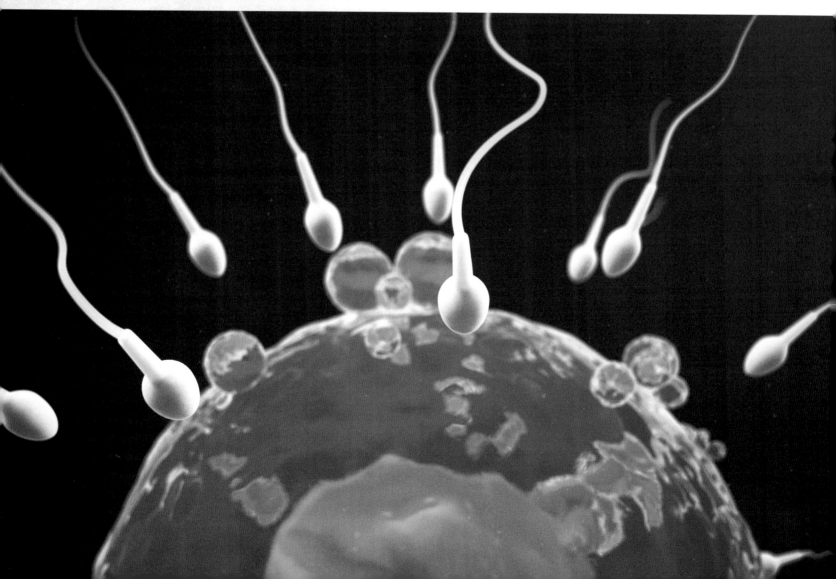

The study of genomes is broadly referred to as genomics and involves a number of distinguishing subfields. One of these areas is called structural genomics or just genomics and typically involves the determination and characterization of the DNA sequence. Another important subfield is called functional genomics, which now involves research studying gene expression in single cells, tissues, organisms, and differing environmental conditions. Another prominent subfield of importance to theoretical evolutionists is called comparative genomics, which relies on the comparison of DNA sequences among organisms in an attempt to determine evolutionary relationships. A related area of research called comparative functional genomics compares gene expression commonalities and differences between organisms. Yet another related field to all of this is an area called proteomics that involves the study of the proteins produced from the genome.

Related to these various "omics" terms I just mentioned are some other connected concepts. For example, a transcriptome represents the expressed RNA complement of a cell or tissue. The term could also describe all identified RNAs discovered in an organism as well. The term proteome refers to the protein complement of a cell, tissue, or a whole organism. The proteome is typically much larger than the organism's gene complement due to the immense variation provided by alternative splicing.

B Appendix
How Genomes Are Sequenced

Claims about nearly identical levels of DNA similarity between humans and chimps are typically given to audiences that have no knowledge of the various aspects of the technology, tricks of the trade, and the extent of the evolutionary dogma that shapes the outcome of any such research. The 2010 human-chimp Y chromosome project used much more thorough genomic techniques to achieve a considerably more detailed and less biased analysis, and the results defied evolution.[1] Then in 2018, a new version of the entire chimp genome was achieved using new long-read DNA sequencing technology, and the results once again debunked evolution by showing that the genomes could be no more than 84% identical at best.[2]

When evaluating evolutionary DNA comparisons between genomes, it is important to understand how the DNA sequence was generated, pieced together, and the pieces arranged before making any authoritative conclusions regarding similarity. This is especially true of all the efforts that have taken place in the construction of the chimp genome over the past 15 years.

One important point to make at the beginning of this discussion is to note the common practice of scientists to arrange a newly obtained DNA sequences of an organism for which little is known previously by utilizing the genome of a supposed closely related organism that has much better developed DNA resources. The guide genome used to stitch together the newly obtained DNA fragments of a novel genome is known as a model or reference genome. The problem is that the assembled sequence will be biased to look like the guide genome used to assemble it.

In the case of comparing the genomes of human and chimp, especially in various versions produced before what is called PanTro6 in 2018, the human genome served as the reference framework to assemble the DNA sequences.[3] The end result is that evolutionary bias has completely permeated the development of what has been traditionally known as the chimpanzee genome. In fact, the scientists who put together the new version of the chimp genome without a human reference acknowledged this fact and called the previous version(s) of the chimp genome "humanized."[3]

History of DNA Sequencing Technology

To fully understand the nature of the huge amount of DNA sequence archived in the world's public databases, it's important to review the history of the technology that produced it. An understanding of this will help explain why different methodologies were used to sequence the DNA of certain types of organisms. It will also provide an understanding of the quality and utility of different types of DNA sequences when comparing genomes. See Figure 1 to see an overall historical timeline of how the technology has progressed.

The modern era of DNA sequencing was kicked off by the research of biologist and chemist Fred Sanger in 1977, which eventually earned him the Nobel Prize.[4] The basic chemistry that Sanger invented, often referred to as Sanger-style sequencing, has been similar in principle until the present time. The initial application of Sanger's technique was very slow and tedious and only very small snippets of DNA could be sequenced in a single experiment. The real genomics revolution, however, occurred by drastically ramping up the basic process using improved chemistries and reagents, the application of robotics to automate sample preparation and sequencing, successive improvements in analysis systems, and continually increasing computer hardware and software developments that were needed to analyze and store the data. All of these overall areas still apply to the newer chemistries that are now being utilized.

Nobel Prize

Over the past decade, a new type of chemistry often referred to as next generation DNA sequencing, or massively parallel sequencing, has drastically increased the overall total DNA sequence output of a single experiment and the public databases in general.[5,6] While this new technology dramatically ramps up the total amount of sequence that can be produced, the main drawback is that the individual snippets of DNA that are produced, called reads, are much shorter than the traditional Sanger-style sequence. Massively parallel sequence reads are on average about 75 to 300 bases in length, while the Sanger-style reads could be up to about 1,700 bases long.

But the technology keeps getting even more interesting as science progresses, and we now have yet another type becoming prevalent that is producing reads up to 200,000 bases in length called long-read sequencing.[7] The only drawback with this new technology is that there tends to be a higher error rate and the sequences are less accurate. Therefore, research will now often include a combination of both long-read and massively parallel sequencing.

The first genomes that were sequenced were from viruses and bacteria because they were small in size and much less complicated than plant or animal genomes. Bacterial genomes are not only very small, they are relatively void of non-protein-coding DNA sequence that can be very difficult to stitch together (assemble) from small DNA reads due to the repetitive sequences they contain.[8,9] Repetitive and non-genic DNA sequences, common in plants and animals, are difficult to assemble into larger contiguous chunks called contigs. Because of these issues, genome sequencing first used small nonrepetitive genomes that were easily assembled, and then scientists advanced to larger animal genomes such as fruit fly, nematode, and human.

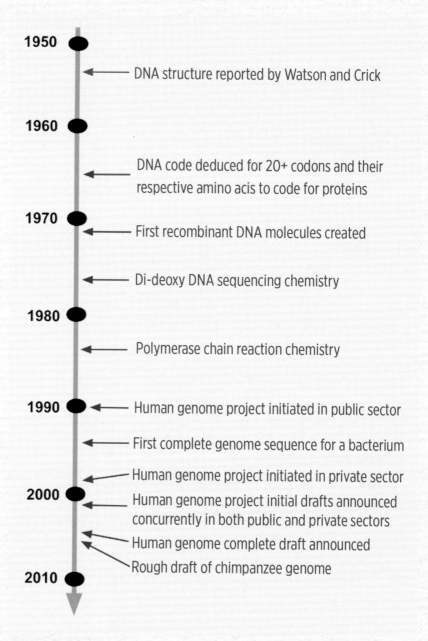

Figure 1. Timeline showing significant milestones related to the history of DNA sequencing

Within the figure:

1950 — DNA structure reported by Watson and Crick

1960

— DNA code deduced for 20+ codons and their respective amino acis to code for proteins

1970 — First recombinant DNA molecules created

— Di-deoxy DNA sequencing chemistry

1980

— Polymerase chain reaction chemistry

1990 — Human genome project initiated in public sector

— First complete genome sequence for a bacterium

— Human genome project initiated in private sector

2000 — Human genome project initial drafts announced concurrently in both public and private sectors

— Human genome complete draft announced

Rough draft of chimpanzee genome

2010

Genetic Maps Help Assemble DNA Sequence

For the human genome project, as well as several other key plant and animal genomes such as nematode and fruit fly, a multi-disciplinary approach was used to accurately sequence the genomes.[10] In this type of approach, a variety of techniques are integrated to create a genetic scaffold that is used to either target specific regions to sequence or to arrange the sequencing reads to reconstruct regions of chromosomes. One of the key parts of a scaffold is called a genetic map that involves the placement of DNA markers across the genome by analyzing how they segregate in the offspring of controlled matings or, in the case of humans, utilizing large multi-generational families.[11] Genetic mapping can create thousands of DNA markers positioned along chromosomes like cities on a state highway map.

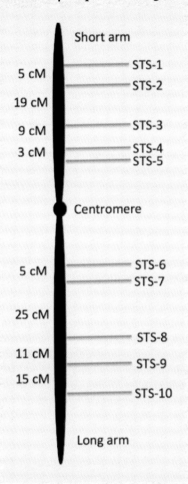

Figure 2. Hypothetical genetic map of a single chromosome showing sequence tagged sites (STS) or genetic markers with recombination-based distances between them demarcated in centimorgans (cM, also referred to as map units)

Physical DNA Clone Maps

Another key component of a genomic framework is called a physical map that provides literal physical distances between landmarks in the genome.[12,13] This technology is based on creating small fragments of chromosomes and then sticking them in a common lab bacteria called *E. coli* in a process called DNA cloning so they can be replicated, maintained (frozen), and studied. These DNA clone libraries are deep frozen for long-term storage. In a highly specialized type of DNA cloning called BAC (bacterial artificial chromosome), very large DNA fragments can be isolated and put into libraries to represent the entire genomes of creatures and is called a genomic BAC library.

While BAC libraries can be used for a variety of purposes, their chief utility is for developing clone maps that are then merged with genetic maps, creating an elaborate framework for genome sequencing. Because the BAC clones and their fragment lengths are known, literal distances in DNA bases between the genetic markers can be calculated. This is analogous to determining the distance in mileage between cities on a road map. Conversely, the clusters of connected BAC clones can be positioned and oriented along chromosomes based on their mapped genetic markers. The end result is a highly accurate framework of the entire genome that can serve as a scaffold for the systematic sequencing or even the specifically targeted sequencing of an organism's DNA.

The whole process of connecting the BACs together and tagging the genetic markers onto them is very technically demanding and also very expensive and time consuming. Therefore, it was only done for projects that had a high priority and received lots of government funding. It's much less common today, but many of the modern genome projects still rely on the frameworks developed years ago.

Sequencing Strategy for the Human Genome Project

The publicly funded part of the human genome project was a global consortium of labs in the USA, England, France, and Japan. Using a comprehensive genomic framework just described, the various labs were each assigned specific sets of BAC clones to sequence in a methodical and highly ordered strategy. Each individual large BAC clone is sequenced by fragmenting it into thousands of little pieces that are then individually sequenced and assembled by a computer. To ramp up the overall process, multiple chromosomal regions were sequenced at the same time. Despite this comprehensive technology and huge global effort, many regions of the human genome remained unsequenced due to their highly

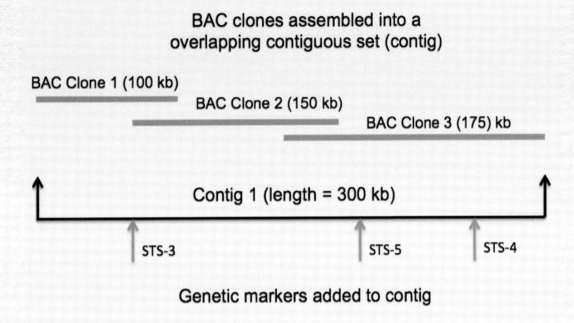

Figure 3. Depiction of a genomic framework for a section of a hypothetical chromosome. The illustration shows how overlapping DNA BAC clones form a contig. The addition of genetic markers to the contig is also shown. This physical-genetic integration forms a genomic framework. Entire chromosomes and genomes can be represented via the development of these frameworks.

repetitive DNA. Only until very recently, with the new long-read sequencing technology mentioned earlier, have these gaps been able to be closed.

The whole process of methodical genome sequencing like that employed in the human genome project is quite involved, time consuming, and extremely expensive. Due to these factors, many DNA sequencing projects and the funding strategies behind them were altered after the human genome and several other model plant and animal genomes were completed.

The Whole Genome Shotgun Sequencing (WGSS) Strategy

While the public side of the human genome project used a methodical framework approach, the corresponding private venture took a different route, with both groups agreeing to publish their first drafts at the same time in 2001 in coordinated publications.[14,15] The maverick research scientist Craig Venter and his private research group used a different approach called whole genome shotgun sequencing, or WGSS.[15] Venter's method bypassed the initial phase of constructing a genomic framework and did not use a methodical bit-by-bit approach to sequencing. Instead, the entire genome was randomly sheared into small pieces all at once, and then the millions of fragments were sequenced en masse.

The huge caveat behind the propaganda surrounding Venter's WGSS so-called shortcut approach was the fact that his project still depended heavily on the use of the genomic framework developed by the public sector to sort out and assemble the incredibly huge amount of random DNA sequences they produced. This behind-the-scenes reality, even though clearly described in Venter's research paper, was never widely popularized in the media. Nevertheless, the general concept of WGSS became very popular and was subsequently used as a cost-effective shortcut strategy for genome sequencing in many different animal, plant, and microbial genomes. The obvious problem with the end product in such WGSS efforts was that the resulting genomes were considerably more fragmented and incomplete.

Construction of the Chimp Genome

The general population is often led to believe that the process of sequencing a genome is a purely objective process free of any evolutionary influence, but this is not always the case. The most dramatic example of this is one that has the greatest impact

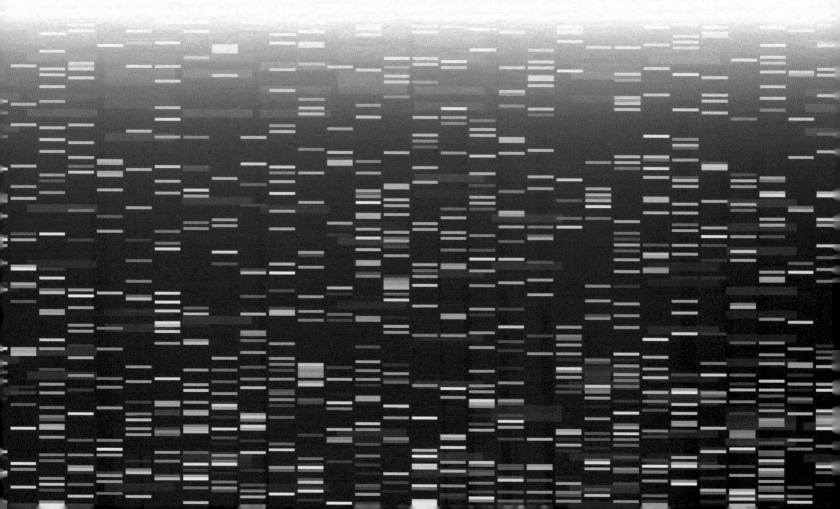

on the issue of human origins—the chimp genome project. Unknown to many people is the fact that the chimpanzee genome was developed as a rough draft and not nearly as complete and detailed as the human genome.[16] In contrast to the human genome effort, funding for the chimp genome was very limited, so the project initially used a WGSS sequencing strategy. However, to sort out and assemble the millions of random DNA fragments, the human genome was used as a framework. In other words, chimp DNA has been organized and put together according to the human genome that was used as a guide. This decision was not only based on convenience but rooted in the assumption that humans evolved from an ape-like ancestor.

One chief concern regarding the use of the human genome as a framework for chimp, outside the obvious evolutionary bias, is the data indicating a major discrepancies in overall size and structure. The average total genome estimate, based on overall DNA content, is that the chimp genome is about 5% larger than human (www.genomesize.com). This was commonly known prior to the days of genome sequencing based on microscopic analyses of chimp chromosomes, which indicated that the overall DNA differences might be more than 10%.

In addition to large differences in the overall amount of DNA, major structural differences, or the way the genes and features are arranged in the genomic landscape, exist between human and chimps.[17] As discussed in the chapter on the issue of incomplete lineage sorting and the chapter on the Y chromosome, many large stretches of DNA cannot be matched up, or if they can, they do not show evolutionary patterns of common ancestry. Unfortunately, these numerous and profound evolutionary anomalies in the way human and chimp genomes are structured have become obfuscated through the use of obscure evolutionary verbiage and data manipulation. These important evolutionary discrepancies never make it to the public realm of knowledge.

In the early days of the genomics and molecular biology revolution, it became evident that humans, apes, and other mammals shared a variety of protein sequences that were similar in their coding sequence. In fact, many human proteins exhibit high amino acid similarity in both ape and non-primate mammalian taxa. The problem is that while certain areas of the genome are similar, the creature-specific areas are not, and this ends up being the type of data that is thrown out or ignored in the evolutionary paradigm. Sadly, a majority of the general public and general scientific community

are not aware of these caveats and still told hold to the evolution-driven dogma that the human genome is 98 to 99% similar to chimpanzee, which we now know to definitely not be the case. The fact is that major differences between the structure of the human and chimp genomes are being documented as the DNA sequencing technology advances and the quality of the genomes improves. As discussed earlier in this book, the human and chimp genomes are no more than 84% identical at best.

When assessing comparisons between genomes and their alleged relatedness, it's important to understand some of the key aspects of how the DNA sequence was obtained, assembled, and manipulated. Along these lines, it has been a very common practice to arrange the newly generated DNA sequence of a creatures for which little is known by using the pre-existing genome of an alleged evolutionary close relative. In some cases where there are different variants or species of the same kind, this approach is justified. In such cases where this is not the case, this obviously produces an evolutionary bias. Understanding the technology and the overriding approaches used to produce a genome is important to consider prior to making any conclusions about the data.

References

1. Hughes, J. F. et al. 2010. Chimpanzee and human Y chromosomes are remarkably divergent in structure and gene content. *Nature.* 463: 536-539.

2. Tomkins, J. P. 2018. Separate Studies Converge on Human-Chimp DNA Dissimilarity. *Acts & Facts* 47 (11): 9.

3. Kronenberg, Z. N. et al. 2018. High-resolution comparative analysis of great ape genomes. *Science.* 360 (6393): eaar6343.

4. Sanger, F., S. Nicklen, and A. R. Coulson. 1977. DNA sequencing with chain-terminating inhibitors. *Proceedings of the National Academy of Sciences.* 12: 5463-5467.

5. Rogers, Y. H. and J. C. Venter. 2005. Massively parallel sequencing. *Nature.* 437: 326-327.

6. Mardis, E. R. 2008. Next-generation sequencing methods. *Annual Review of Genomics and Human Genetics.* 9: 387-402.

7. Nakano, K. et al. 2017. Advantages of genome sequencing by long-read sequencer using SMRT technology in medical area. *Human Cell.* 30 (3): 149-161.

8. Fraser, C. M. et al. 1995. The minimal gene complement of *Mycoplasma genitalium. Science.* 270: 397-403.

9. Mushegian, A. R. and E. V. Koonan. 1996. A minimal gene set for cellular life derived by comparison of complete bacterial genomes. *Proceedings of the National Academy of Sciences.* 93: 10268-10273.

10. International Human Genome Sequencing Consortium. 2004. Finishing the euchromatic sequence of the human genome. *Nature.* 431: 931-945.

11. Kong, A. et al. 2002. A high-resolution recombination map of the human genome. *Nature Genetics.* 31: 241-247.

12. Meyers, B. C., S. Scalabrin, and M. Morgante. 2004. Mapping and sequencing complex genomes: Let's get physical. *Nature Reviews Genetics.* 5: 578-589.

13. Warren, R. L. et al. 2010. Physical map assisted whole-genome shotgun assemblies. *Genome Research.* 16: 768-775.

14. International Human Genome Sequencing Consortium. 2001. Initial sequencing and analysis of the human genome. *Nature.* 409: 861-920.

15. Venter, J. C. et al. 2001. The sequence of the human genome. *Science.* 291: 1304-1351.

16. The Chimpanzee Sequencing and Analysis Consortium. 2005. Initial sequence of the chimpanzee genome and comparison with the human genome. *Nature.* 437: 69-87.

17. Newman, T. L. et al. 2005. A genome-wide survey of structural variation between human and chimpanzee. *Genome Research.* 15: 1344-1356.

C Appendix

Human-Chimp Genome Updates

Ongoing genetic research continually makes new discoveries undermining the evolutionary story of human and chimp descent from a common ancestor. Following are just a few examples of the more recent research results supporting the unique creation of humans.

3-D Human Genome Is Radically Different from Chimp

All plant and animal genomes studied so far exhibit complex and distinct three-dimensional (3-D) structures in their chromosome configurations depending on the type of cell (e.g., heart, liver, brain, etc.). Given the incredible variability among genome configurations within a single type of creature, let alone that which exists between creatures (e.g., human versus chimpanzee), this area of evolutionary comparison has been difficult for secular researchers. A study published in *Trends in Genetics* evaluates research in this emerging field and shows the human 3-D genome is distinctly unique to humans, confirming previous research that showed it is as different compared to chimp as it is to mouse.[1]

One of the best ways to empirically understand the 3-D configuration of chromosomes in the nucleus of the cell is to define topologically associating domains (TADs) in the DNA sequence. TADs are characterized as regions whose DNA sequences preferentially contact and interact with each other in association with specific cell types and biological functions. TADs were first discovered in 2012 using newly developed chro-

Wood mouse

mosome conformation analysis techniques.[2] In mammals, the median TAD length is about 900,000 DNA letters (bases) long—a sizeable stretch of DNA that typically contains multiple genes and many regulatory switches and control features.[3]

One important aspect of 3-D genome structure has to do with the epigenetic modification of proteins called histones that the DNA is wrapped around. A 2011 study showed that a specific type of histone modification had only about a 70% overlap or similarity between humans and chimps.[4] Remarkably, another study in 2012 showed

that humans had about a 70% similarity for the same feature with mice.[5] In other words, humans were as different to mice as they were to chimps for this particular genome conformation metric.

In the *Trends in Genetics* study, scientists wanted to take a closer look at this evolutionary anomaly to see if it held true for one of the most important features of genome conformation—TAD similarity. They found that in comparing humans and chimps, "only ~43% of TADs conserved [similar] between these species, but across many different parameters (e.g., resolution, window size, genome assembly) and different downstream analysis decisions, no more than 78% of domains and 83% of TAD boundaries were found to be shared between humans and chimpanzees." This huge evolutionary discrepancy led them to conclude, "In our mind, there is no strong basis for the common and often unchallenged notion that TADs are highly conserved."[1] In other words, a lack of conservation means no evidence for evolution.

This study, along with many others, is continuing to debunk evolution and confirm the uniqueness of the human genome. For example, previous research by this author has shown that the human and chimp genomes are no more than 85% similar, and it's likely the final findings will be far less than that.[6] The Bible clearly states that humans were created uniquely in the image of God.[7] Modern genetics research increasingly confirms this profound truth.

Human Genome 20th Anniversary—Junk DNA Hits the Trash

The first rough drafts of the human genome were reported in 2001 (one in the private sector and one in the public sector).[8,9] Since then, after 20 years of intensive globally conducted research, the data have revealed a wealth of complexity that has completely upset all of the original evolutionary misconceptions.[10] Most importantly, the false evolutionary paradigm of "junk DNA" has been utterly debunked in favor of a new model, one containing pervasive functionality and network complexity. The reality of this seemingly unending complexity is only just beginning to be revealed—an inconvenient fact that points directly to an omnipotent Creator.

A cover story in the journal *Nature* briefly summarized the past 20 years since the original publications of the first drafts of the human genome hit the press.[10] When the first phase of research was completed in 2001, it was initially found that the genome contained about 25,000 protein-coding genes and that the actual coding segments of these genes only accounted for about 2% of the total DNA sequence. Many evolutionists found affirmation in these initial reports. This was because the neutral model of evolutionary theory predicted that there should be vast regions of the human genome in evolutionary limbo (termed "junk DNA"). These alleged nonfunctional regions would then be randomly churning out new genes for nature to magically select.[11,12] Needless to say, this misguided evolutionary speculation was short-lived.

Since 2001, numerous research projects have demonstrated that these uncharted and mysterious regions of the human genome were not junk at all. Rather, they were vital to life and good health. In a subsection of the 2021 *Nature* article titled "Not Junk," the authors say, "With the HGP [human genome project] draft in hand, the discovery of non-protein-coding elements exploded. So far, that growth has outstripped the discovery of protein-coding genes by a factor of five, and shows no signs of slowing." They also said, "Thanks in large part to the HGP, it is now appreciated that the majority of functional sequences in the human genome do not encode proteins. Rather, elements such as long non-coding RNAs, promoters, enhancers and countless gene-regulatory motifs work together to bring the genome to life."[10]

The main points of the past 20 years of research on the human genome can be summarized as follows:

1. The human genome is a complete storehouse of important information, and this fact negates the concept of junk DNA.
2. Protein-coding genes are largely a basic set of instructions within a complex and larger repertoire of regulatory DNA sequence.
3. Many more genes exist (compared to protein-coding genes) that code for functional RNA molecules that are not used to make proteins but do other jobs in the cell.
4. A vast number of regulatory switches and control features exists in the human genome that regulates its function.

Indigenous people in the mountains of Peru

The pervasive and complex design of the human genome is exactly what's gleaned from the Bible. After all, Psalm 139:14 says, "I will praise You, for I am fearfully and wonderfully made; marvelous are Your works, and that my soul knows very well."

Human High-Altitude Habitation Reveals Adaptive Design

Humans have the remarkable ability to inhabit high altitudes where living conditions are especially harsh and challenging. A study in *Genome Biology and Evolution* has shown that specifically directed epigenetic modifications to various places in the genome are an important heritable adaptive mechanism in conferring this unique ability.[13] These new results utterly refute the false Darwinian paradigm of natural selection, revealing innate systems of complex biological engineering that undergird high-altitude adaptation.

Humans have colonized an amazing array of challenging environments across the earth, from arid deserts to frozen tundra, tropical rainforests, and some of the highest mountain regions. Among these environs, high-altitude mountain living is one of the most challenging situations. Nevertheless, approximately 2% of the world's people permanently inhabit high-altitude regions over 2,500 meters (1.5 miles) above sea level.

In these places, oxygen is sparse, ultraviolet radiation is high, and temperatures are low. Examples of people groups that live at these extreme altitudes include native Andeans, Tibetans, Mongolians, and Ethiopians. Studies of Andeans and Tibetans have revealed an increase in chest circumference (associated with greater lung volume), elevated oxygen saturation, and a low hypoxic ventilatory response in contrast to lowlanders who travel to high altitudes and have an intense hypoxic ventilatory response to the lower levels of oxygen.[13,14]

For years, biologists have been trying to find a genetic component to this unique suite of adaptive high-altitude responses—but with only moderate success. Previous studies have shown a propensity for a few different gene variants to exist at higher frequencies in high-altitude populations, but nothing definitive has been found as to a significant and consistent heritable genetic mechanism that would explain the unique changes in physiology and anatomy. As one secular author stated, "The underlying mechanism for this remains poorly understood."[15]

The new *Genome Biology and Evolution* study, however, has revealed for the first time an exciting feature of built-in adaptive design based on the broadening field of epigenetics research. While epigenetics is a diverse field of research, one popular sector within it studies the addition of methyl molecule tags that are strategically placed on cytosine bases throughout the DNA in and around genes to regulate their expression, a process known as methylation. These methyl tags do not change the DNA sequence itself but modify how the DNA is functionally utilized, resulting in a diversity of downstream changes in physiology and development. Furthermore, these methylation patterns can be inherited for several generations so that succeeding populations are automatically primed for the specific environment they will live in.

In this research, the authors compared the DNA methylation patterns of a specific people group of highland Quechua ancestry in the Andes region of South America. They included people who lived at high altitudes, those who lived at low altitudes, and those who migrated from low to high. First, the researchers discovered that many of these adaptive epigenetic modifications were associated with genes involved in red blood cell production, glucose metabolism, and skeletal muscle development. These are standard gene regions connected to high-altitude adaptation.

Second, they found that the whole process of epigenetic-based adaptation to high altitudes was triggered early during embryonic development so that children were born fully adapted with bigger lungs and other important needed traits. This phenomenon is known as developmental adaptation or adaptive plasticity. In other words, a huge array of developmental sensors detects key features of the environment and conveys data that are processed by specialized cellular machinery to modify the organism's genome with strategically placed methyl tags. The methyl tags then properly control and guide the development of a high-altitude-adapted baby.

While evolutionists have traditionally regarded high-altitude adaptation in humans as evidence of natural selection, the new study exposes the complete futility of this Darwinian anti-design paradigm. Natural selection purports that nature has the volition and capability to select beneficial traits based on a set of DNA mutation options. In reality, the environment (nature) merely represents a set of parameters (temperature, oxygen content, etc.) that engineered living systems detect and track through elaborate sensors. These data are then processed through exceedingly complex internal systems that ultimately provide highly specified outputs and solutions resulting in adaptation.

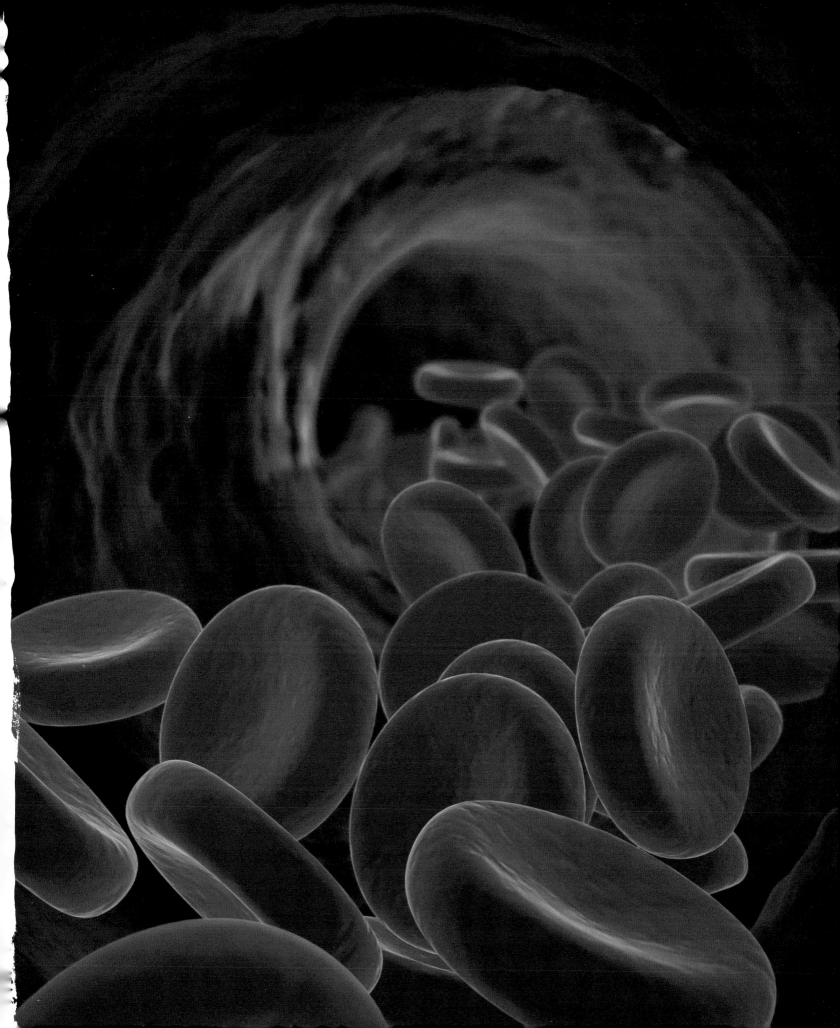

God's creatures are able to adapt to a wide variety of very different environments because they were fabulously designed and engineered by our omnipotent Creator, Jesus Christ

This study simply reiterates the obvious fact that we should be doing biology as if Charles Darwin and his anti-design imposter (natural selection) for God the Creator had never existed. Creatures adapt to diverse environments because they were fabulously designed and engineered by an omnipotent Creator—the Lord Jesus Christ.

References

1. Eres, I. E. and Y. Gilad. 2021. A TAD Skeptic: Is 3D Genome Topology Conserved? *Trends in Genetics*. 37 (3): 216-223.
2. Dixon, J. R. et al. 2012. Topological domains in mammalian genomes identified by analysis of chromatin interactions. *Nature*. 485 (7398): 376-380.
3. Yu, M. and B. Ren. 2017. The Three-Dimensional Organization of Mammalian Genomes. *Annual Review of Cell and Developmental Biology*. 33: 265-289.
4. Cain, C. E. et al. 2011. Gene Expression Differences Among Primates Are Associated With Changes in a Histone Epigenetic Modification. *Genetics*. 187 (4): 1225-1234.
5. Woo, Y. H. and W.-H. Li. 2012. Evolutionary Conservation of Histone Modifications in Mammals. *Molecular Biology and Evolution*. 29 (7): 1757-1767.
6. Tomkins, J. P. 2018. Separate Studies Converge on Human-Chimp DNA Dissimilarity. *Acts & Facts*. 47 (11): 9.
7. Genesis 1:27.
8. Venter, J. C. et al. 2001. The Sequence of the Human Genome. *Science*. 291 (2001): 1304-1351.
9. International Human Genome Sequencing Consortium. 2001. Initial Sequencing and Analysis of the Human Genome. *Nature*. 409 (2001): 860-921.
10. Gates, A. J. et al. 2021. A wealth of discovery built on the Human Genome Project—by the numbers. *Nature*. 590: 212-215.
11. Tomkins, J. P. 2017. Evolutionary Clock Futility. *Acts & Facts*. 46 (3): 16.
12. Tomkins, J. P. and J. Bergman. 2015. Evolutionary molecular genetic clocks—a perpetual exercise in futility and failure. *Journal of Creation*. 29 (2): 26-35.
13. Childebayeva, A. et al. 2021. Genome-Wide Epigenetic Signatures of Adaptive Developmental Plasticity in the Andes. *Genome Biology and Evolution*. 13 (2): evaa239.
14. Thomas, B. Highlander Tibetans Show Adaptation, Not 'Natural Selection.' *Creation Science Update*. Posted on ICR.org July 15, 2010, accessed March 2, 2021.
15. McGrath, C. 2021. Highlight: The Epigenetics of Life at 12,000 ft. *Genome Biology and Evolution*. 13 (2): evaa266.

IMAGE CREDITS

Baylor College of Medicine: 24

Bigstock: cover, 20, 29, 31, 41, 47, 58, 63, 65-66, 71, 74-75, 78, 81-82, 84, 86-87, 91-92, 94, 99, 102, 104, 109, 111, 114, 117, 119, 122-123, 128, 130, 132-137, 139-140, 142-144, 147-148, 151-152, 155, 158, 160, 162, 164-165, 167-168, 171-172

iStockphoto: 21-22, 35, 44, 53, 107

Thomas, Brian: 121 top

Tomkins, Jeffrey P.: 30, 49, 50, 52, 55, 59, 101, 115, 156-157, 159

Windsor, Susan: 110

INDEX

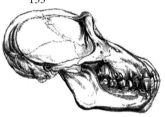

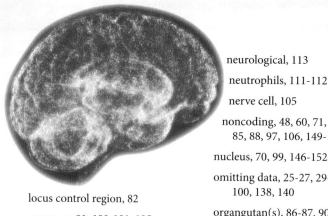

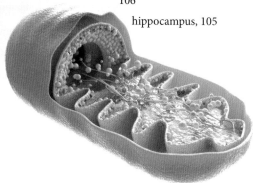

ABOUT THE AUTHOR

 **Dr. Jeffrey P. Tomkins** earned a master's degree in plant science in 1990 from the University of Idaho, where he performed research in plant hormones. He received his Ph.D. in genetics from Clemson University in 1996. While at Clemson, he worked as a research technician in a plant breeding/genetics program, with a research focus in the area of quantitative and physiological genetics in soybean. After receiving his Ph.D., he worked at a genomics institute and became a faculty member in the Department of Genetics and Biochemistry at Clemson. He became a Christian as an undergraduate at Washington State University in 1982, with a goal to eventually work as a scientist and author in the creation science field. In 2009, Dr. Tomkins joined the Institute for Creation Research as Research Associate. He was appointed Director of Life Sciences in 2016 and Director of Research in 2020. He is the primary author of *The Design and Complexity of the Cell* and a contributor to *Guide to Creation Basics* and *Creation Basics & Beyond*.

ABOUT THE INSTITUTE FOR CREATION RESEARCH

After 50 years of ministry, the Institute for Creation Research remains a leader in scientific research within the context of biblical creation. Founded by Dr. Henry Morris in 1970, ICR exists to conduct scientific research within the realms of origins and Earth history and then to educate the public both formally and informally through professional training programs, through conferences and seminars around the country, and through books, magazines, and media presentations. ICR was established for three main purposes:

Dr. Henry Morris

Research. ICR conducts laboratory, field, theoretical, and library research on projects that seek to understand the science of origins and Earth history. ICR scientists have conducted multi-year research projects at key locations such as Grand Canyon, Mount St. Helens, Yosemite Valley, Santa Cruz River Valley in Argentina, and on vital issues like Radioisotopes and the Age of the Earth (RATE), Flood-Activated Sedimentation and Tectonics (FAST), the human genome, soft tissue in fossils, and other topics related to geology, genetics, astro/geophysics, paleoclimatology, paleobiochemistry, and much more.

Education. ICR offers formal courses of instruction and conducts seminars and workshops, as well as other means of instruction. With 40 years' experience in education, first through our California-based science education program (1981–2010) and now with programs offered through the School of Biblical Apologetics, ICR trains men and women to do real-world apologetics with a foundation of biblical authority and creation science. ICR's online programs include a one-year, non-degree training program for professionals called the Creationist Worldview and an Origins Matter Short Course series. Additionally, ICR scientists and staff speak to numerous groups each year through seminars and conferences, as well as offering live science presentations at the ICR Discovery Center for Science & Earth History.

Communication. ICR produces books, videos, periodicals, and other media for communicating the evidence and information related to its research and education. ICR's central publication is *Acts & Facts*, a free full-color monthly magazine with a readership of over 250,000, providing articles relevant to science, apologetics, education, and worldview issues. ICR also publishes the daily devotional *Days of Praise* with over 500,000 readers worldwide. Our website at ICR.org features regular and relevant creation science updates. The three radio programs produced by ICR can be heard on outlets around the world, and we make our materials available through multiple social media outlets.

Headquartered in Dallas, Texas, ICR's latest outreach is the ICR Discovery Center for Science & Earth History, with cutting-edge exhibits, planetarium shows, and live science presentations. The Institute for Creation Research continues to expand its work and influence, endeavoring to encourage Christians with the wonders of God's creation.

P. O. Box 59029
Dallas, Texas 75229
ICR.org

800.337.0375 (main) | 800.628.7640 (customer service)

IN-DEPTH SCIENCE FROM ICR

Explore the creation-evolution debate with ICR's In-Depth Science books. In *Rethinking Radiometric Dating: Evidence for a Young Earth from a Nuclear Physicist*, Dr. Vernon Cupps examines the major radiometric dating methods and the significant problems with the dating methodology that many scientists use to argue for a billions-of-years-old earth.

In *Carved in Stone: Geological Evidence of the Worldwide Flood*, Dr. Timothy Clarey utilizes drill and seismic data to demonstrate that rather than reflecting millions of years, the rock record reflects a progressive, year-long global flood that occurred just thousands of years ago.

In *The Ice Age and Climate Change: A Creation Perspective*, Dr. Jake Hebert examines climate science and finds flawed theories, circular reasoning, and conclusions based on outdated data and uniformitarian preconceptions. Christians have good biblical and scientific reasons to reject climate change alarmism.

ICR's In-Depth Science resources show that not only does the scientific evidence *not* support evolution, it strongly affirms the biblical account of creation and the Flood.

Find out more about these books and other resources at **ICR.org/store**.

ICR.org

THE DESIGN AND COMPLEXITY OF THE CELL

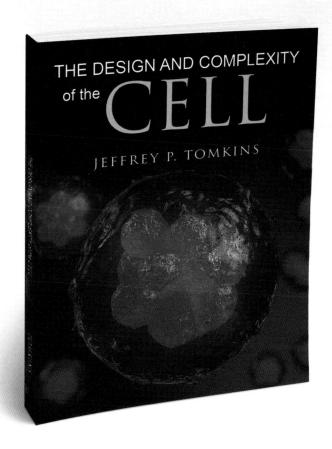

There's nothing simple about the cell. Its complexity is far superior to anything a human mind could imagine or conceive—it could not have just evolved over billions of years through random processes. The more scientists delve into the mysteries of the cell, the more exquisite design they discover.

ICR geneticist Dr. Jeffrey Tomkins and his contributing colleagues reveal in *The Design and Complexity of the Cell* how marvelously the cell was made by God. Understanding the basics of cell biology and its support for the biblical account of creation will not only build your faith, it will also provide a powerful tool for evangelism and the defense of that faith.

Find out more about this book and other resources at **ICR.org/store**.

ICR.org

RESOURCES FROM ICR

Creation or evolution? This debate is one of the most vital issues of our time. ICR's original DVD series present the evidence that confirms the biblical account of creation and provide defensible answers to questions of faith and science. Ideal for group study, these compelling and engaging presentations demonstrate that not only does the scientific evidence *not* support evolution, it strongly affirms the accuracy and authority of God's Word.

Find out more about these DVD series and other resources at **ICR.org/store**.

INSTITUTE FOR
CREATION
RESEARCH

ICR.org

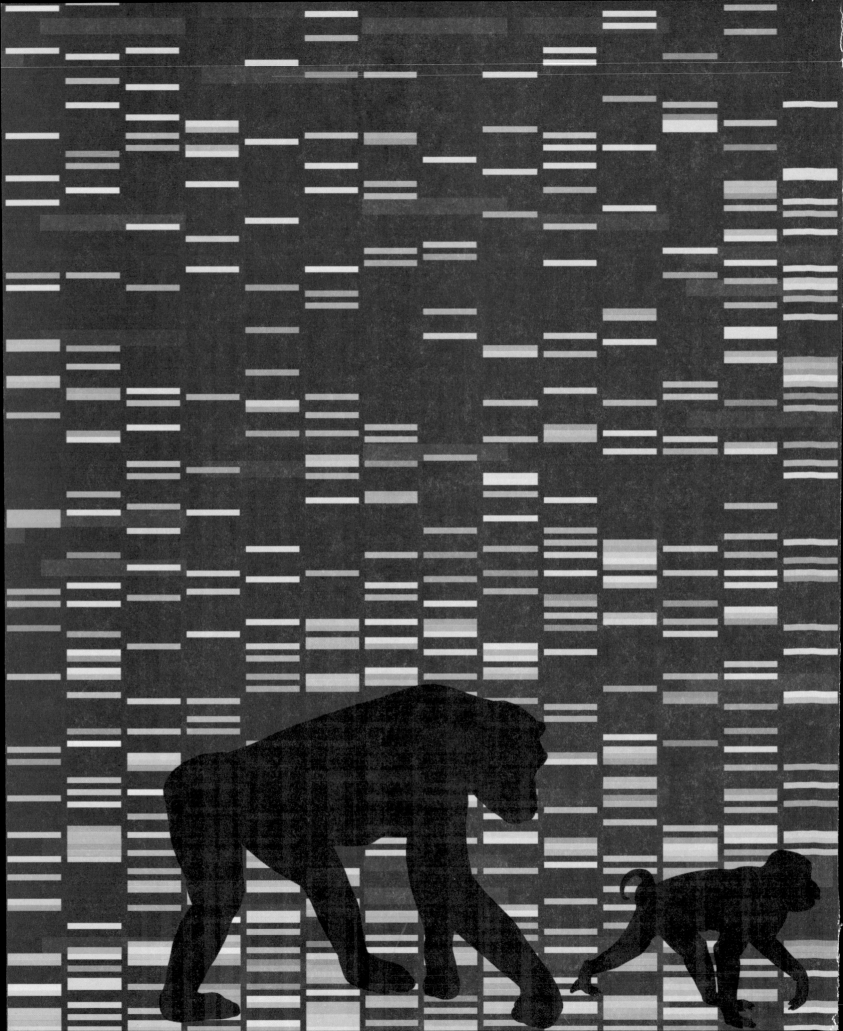